Ionization Constants

Ionization Constants

OF ACIDS AND BASES

*

A LABORATORY MANUAL

by

ADRIEN ALBERT
D.Sc. (Lond.), F.R.I.C., F.A.A.

Professor of Medical Chemistry in the
Australian National University, Canberra

and

E. P. SERJEANT

University of New South Wales,
Sydney

London: Methuen & Co Ltd
New York: John Wiley & Sons Inc

First published 1962
© *1962 Adrien Albert & E. P. Serjeant*
Printed in Great Britain
by Butler & Tanner Ltd
Frome and London
Cat. No. (Methuen) 2/4086/11

3.75

Contents

Contents

Contents

Contents

Preface

This practical manual is intended for those who, without previous experience, wish to determine an ionization constant. In addition, some more advanced instruction is provided for those who wish to extend their range of techniques, or to tackle more difficult examples.

Much time can be saved in calculations if one knows how to set out the results. Hence we have given many worked examples for which only easily procurable substances have been used. We strongly advise the beginner to repeat, in the order printed, each worked example, both the practical work and the calculations. He should begin by titrating boric acid (as on p. 33) until all his pK_a values, in a single titration, fall within the given spread. Not until all six examples in Chapter 2 can be performed satisfactorily, should any unknowns be tackled.

A more advanced worker may prefer to begin with glycine (p. 39). If his results all fall within the given spread, he should go on to the examples of Chapters 3 and 4.

Our first examples require only a few, very simple calculations. We have taken care to explain when these simple methods will not suffice and exactly what refinements of calculation are called for. We have introduced the more complicated calculations as gradually as possible, and with full explanatory detail.

Help in the interpretation of ionization constants is provided. It is shown how these are related to solubility (Chapter 6), how the degree of ionization at any pH can be calculated (Appendix IV), and how ionization constants can aid in deciphering an unknown structure (Chapter 8). A selection of 400 known constants is set out in tables with commentary (pp. 121–153).

Because this is a practical manual, we have touched only lightly on the theory of ionization (Chapter 1) and refer the

Preface

reader to R. P. Bell's *Acids and Bases* and V. Gold's *pH Measurements*, in the Methuen Chemical Monographs. Robinson and Stokes' *Electrolyte Solutions* (London, Butterworth, 1959) is recommended for further study.

Our last chapter deals with the determination of the stability constants of metal complexes by measuring the expulsion of protons as the complexes are formed. The potentiometric techniques of Chapters 2 and 3 are readily applied to these problems.

Throughout the book we have tried to set acceptable standards for accuracy, neither discouragingly hard to attain nor yet so lax that the results are meaningless. Only in laboratories devoted to obtaining constants of the very highest accuracy can the ultimate refinements of technique be learnt, and we cannot hope to teach these in a book. On the other hand we are disturbed by the many highly inaccurate results which yearly appear in the literature, and we hope that this book can give guidance in avoiding the commoner pitfalls.

We thank Dr D. D. Perrin for helpful suggestions, Mr K. Tratt for the drawings, and Miss P. L. Baetens for typing the manuscript.

A.A.
E.P.S.

1

Introduction

What is meant by the term 'Ionization Constants'

In this book, the term Ionization Constants means those constants which are used to measure the strength of acids and bases. They are often loosely referred to as Dissociation Constants, but this term is too vague because ionization forms only a small corner of the vast field of dissociation phenomena. Thus substrates dissociate from enzymes, micelles dissociate into monomers, and above 700° iodine molecules dissociate into iodine atoms. Many other such equilibrium processes are known and much scientific effort goes into determining the appropriate dissociation constants, but the majority of these dissociations are not ionizations. On the other hand, zwitterions are ionized but they are not dissociated. Hence the term dissociation constant is not a suitable synonym for our purpose, although it is still occasionally used.

A minor objection to the term ionization constants is that the constant for a *base* represents an equilibrium in which one ion gives rise to another (see equation (1.5) on p. 6). This difficulty disappears if we define the term ionization constants as referring to hydrogen and hydroxyl ions only. Another term, Acidity Constant, has been proposed (for both acids and bases) to meet the difficulty raised by equation (1.5). However this term has not yet found wide acceptance. We prefer the term Ionization Constants as a measure of the strength of both acids and bases.

Why ionization constants are determined

Ionization constants reveal the proportions of the different ionic species into which a substance is divided at any chosen pH. Thus,

1

when one reads that the ionization constant of benzoic acid is 7.6×10^{-5}, one can quickly calculate that at pH 5 it is 89% in the form of anion (I) and 11% in the form of neutral molecule (II). This kind of information is useful in many ways. For example different ionic species have different ultraviolet spectra, and significant spectrophotometry can be done only when this is kept in mind. The ionic species of a given substance differ in other physical properties also, and in chemical and biological properties as well.* Ionization constants, by defining the pH range in which a substance is least ionized, indicate the conditions under which it can be isolated in maximal yield (see Chapter 6) and this has great value in preparative chemistry.

Ionization constants are often used to help diagnose the structure of a newly isolated substance (see Chapter 8), and they can help to confirm the identity of two substances which have no melting point.

(I)   (II)

A brief summary of the chemistry of ionization

Equation (1.1) illustrates the kind of equilibria for which ionization constants are determined.

$$HA \rightleftharpoons H^+ + A^- \tag{1.1}$$

Thus, the dissociation of acetic acid (CH_3CO_2H) in aqueous solution gives hydrogen ions (H^+) and acetate ions ($CH_3CO_2^-$), and these form an equilibrium mixture. Before discussing the quantitative aspects of this equilibrium, a brief account of the general chemistry of ionization will be presented.

Many substances do not increase the electrical conductivity of water when dissolved in it. These are called non-electrolytes, and they depress the freezing point of water proportionally to

* See ALBERT, *Selective Toxicity*. London: Methuen, 1960.

their molar concentration. Ether, chloroform and benzene are familiar examples of non-electrolytes.

Acids, bases and salts, on the other hand, all increase the electrical conductivity of water when dissolved in it. Such substances are called electrolytes. All electrolytes depress the freezing point of water to a greater extent than would have been expected from their molar concentration. For example, hydrochloric acid, sodium hydroxide and sodium chloride all cause twice the expected depression. This phenomenon led the Swedish chemist Arrhenius to formulate the theory of ionization of electrolytes (1884–7) which was refined later by Brönsted, Lowry, Debye and others.*

This theory postulates that in aqueous solution there are no molecules of sodium chloride, but only sodium cations and chloride anions; no molecules of hydrogen chloride but only hydrogen cations and chloride anions; and no molecules of sodium hydroxide but only sodium cations and hydroxyl anions. Concentrated solutions (e.g. stronger than 0·01M) show a departure from ideal behaviour not due to the formation of neutral molecules but because of interionic attractions and repulsions of various kinds.

Sodium sulphate gives three times the depression expected for the molecule Na_2SO_4, and it has been shown that it is split into three ions, namely two sodium cations and one sulphate anion (SO_4^{2+}).

In general, all salts are completely ionized in aqueous solution† although there are some exceptions such as the halides of mercury, cadmium and lead. Polyvalent metallic cations form complexes with oxalic acid, phosphoric acid, glycine and other ligands which are usually ring systems (as discussed under Chelation in Chapter 9). These are not salts and have little tendency to ionize.

Unlike salts, many acids and bases are not completely ionized in solution. Strong acids and strong bases (e.g. sodium hydroxide

---

* See BELL, *Acids and Bases*. London: Methuen, 1952.
† BRÖNSTED, *Physical Chemistry*. London: Heinemann, 1937

and hydrochloric acid) are completely ionized in the pH range 0–14. But weak and moderately strong acids and bases are ionized only incompletely although they ionize more completely in dilute than in concentrated solutions. Moreover salts formed from a weak acid, or from a weak base, are not stable in solution, but hydrolyse partly to the acids and bases from which they are derived. In this way a salt (which by definition is completely ionized) can give rise to an acid or base which is incompletely ionized. Because these are all rapid equilibrium processes, this situation is not so complex as it may seem. Indeed, the degree of ionization in solution depends on only two factors, the pH and the pK. The latter, defined below in (1.3), is a constant for any given acid or base. Hence, if the pH is controlled, the degree of ionization depends only on the nature of the acid (or base) concerned, regardless of whether or not it has previously been neutralized. For example, the same *ratio* of acetate ions to acetic acid molecules results from the addition of sodium acetate, potassium acetate, or acetic acid to water that has been buffered at a given pH. If the pH of the solution is raised, the proportion of ions to molecules will increase, but the new ratio will again be independent of whether acetic acid or an acetate was used. That this must be so follows from the law of mass action.

The essential part of any theory of ionization is the application of the law of mass action to describe the state of ionic equilibrium. Thus the product of the concentration of the *ions* derived from the ionization of acetic acid always bears a fixed ratio to the concentration of the non-ionized *molecules*. That is to say $[H^+][CH_3CO_2^-]$ bears a fixed ratio to $[CH_3CO_2H]$. This ratio is called the acidic ionization constant (K_a), or more simply the ionization constant. Thus

$$K_a = \frac{[H^+][CH_3CO_2^-]}{[CH_3CO_2H]} \qquad (1.2)$$

and this has been found by experiment to be $1 \cdot 75 \times 10^{-5}$ moles per litre at 20°C. For the sake of brevity 'moles per litre' is usually omitted. To define the ionization of any acid, equation (1.2) can be

Introduction

expressed in the general form

$$K_a = \frac{[H^+][A^-]}{[HA]}$$

whence $\qquad pK_a = pH + \log[HA] - \log[A^-]$ \hfill (1.3)

Where A^- is any given anion and p means the negative logarithm.*
It will be realized that in aqueous solution the three components
of the equilibrium are hydrated, thus H^+ is used as an abbreviation for H_3^+O or (H^+,H_2O).

Classical and thermodynamic constants

Equation (1.3) is only an approximation, because the law of mass
action is based on the concept of 'active mass' as opposed to
concentrations. Thus we should more correctly write

$$K_a^T = \frac{a_{H^+} \cdot a_{A^-}}{a_{HA}}, \quad \text{more conveniently written as} \quad \frac{\{H^+\}\{A^-\}}{\{HA\}} \quad (1.4)$$

where a_{H^+}, a_{A^-} and a_{HA} refer to the activities of the three species
involved. The implication of equation (1.4) is that not all of any
species in (1.3) is completely free. It is known from physical
properties that this departure from the ideal state increases as the
concentration is increased. The K_a of equation (1.3) is therefore
called the *concentration ionization constant* (K_a^C) because it varies
with the dilution.† The K_a^T of equation (1.4) is called the *thermodynamic constant*, and is independent of concentration. At infinite
dilution, the concentration constant becomes numerically equal
to the thermodynamic constant. For univalent acids and bases,
the difference between the two constants is usually small in 0·01
molar, and almost non-existent in 0·001 molar, concentrations.
These differences are dealt with in Chapter 3 (p. 43), and help
is given in deciding when allowance must be made for activity
effects (p. 57). We recommend equation (1.3), for the sake of

* For the purposes of Chapters 1 and 2, pH may be taken as the negative
logarithm of the hydrogen ion concentration. A more exact definition is
given by equation (3.9) (p. 59).
† This concentration constant is sometimes called the 'classical constant',
and it is related to the 'apparent constant' (K′), but both are undesirable
terms.

simplicity, provided that: (*a*) constants be determined in solutions not stronger than 0·01 molar, and (*b*) only univalent ions be dealt with.

For the present it need only be noted that the activity of a neutral molecule does not differ appreciably from its concentration, at any dilution; and that pH, as commonly measured, is a better measure of hydrogen ion activity than of hydrogen ion concentration, although these two quantities do not usually differ greatly. Hence [A⁻] is the only strange term in the equation (1.4).

Bases

The state of ionic equilibria of bases also can be described by acidic ionization constants. For example, ammonia is a base which can take up a hydrogen ion to form an ammonium ion. This is equivalent to thinking of the ammonium ion (NH_4^+) as a weak acid which partly ionizes in water to give hydrogen ions (H^+) and molecules of ammonia (NH_3), thus

$$K_a = \frac{[H^+][NH_3]}{[NH_4^+]} \tag{1.5}$$

This has been found by experiment to be $5\cdot5 \times 10^{-10}$ at 25°. Equation (1.5) may be written more generally

$$K_a = \frac{[H^+][B]}{[BH^+]} \tag{1.6}$$

This use of acidic constants for the ionization of bases was introduced by Brönsted in 1923, who saw that it would be advantageous to have the ionization of acids and bases expressed on the same scale, just as pH is used for alkalinity as well as acidity. There is a formal similarity between (1.3) and (1.6): the species in the bottom line, in each case, ionizes to furnish a hydrogen ion and a new species which is the original substance minus the hydrogen ion. Earlier workers used a different constant (K_b) for the ionization of bases. Thus for ammonia

$$K_b = \frac{[OH^-][NH_4^+]}{[NH_3,H_2O]} \tag{1.7}$$

and K_b was found experimentally to be $1\cdot 8 \times 10^{-5}$ at $25°$. All use of K_b is to be avoided, because it does not touch the heart of the matter which is this: an acid produces hydrogen ions and a base receives them. Thus both acid and base should be related in terms of a single quantity, their affinity for the hydrogen ion. Such a relationship requires the use of the acidic constant (K_a) for both acids and bases.

pK values

Ionization constants are small and inconvenient figures and hence it has become customary to use their negative logarithms (known as pK_a values) which are convenient both in speech and writing (see equation 1.3). Thus the pK_a of acetic acid is $4\cdot 76$, which is a more convenient expression than the ionization constant $1\cdot 75 \times 10^{-5}$. Again, the pK_a of ammonia is $9\cdot 26$, which is more convenient than the ionization constant ($5\cdot 5 \times 10^{-10}$). The older literature gave pK_b values for bases (e.g. $4\cdot 74$ for ammonia at $25°$); these can be converted to pK_a values by subtraction from the negative logarithm of the ionic product of water (K_w) at the temperature of determination. The value of pK_w is $14\cdot 17$ at $20°$, $14\cdot 00$ at $25°$ and $13\cdot 62$ at $37°$ (see Appendix II). Thus

$$pK_a + pK_b = 14\cdot 17 \text{ at } 20° \qquad (1.8)$$

It is evident that pK_a values provide a very convenient way of comparing the strength of acids (or of bases). The stronger an acid is, the lower its pK_a; the stronger a base is, the higher its pK_a.

The shape of a titration curve. When an acid or base is half ionized in solution, it has a pH equal to its pK_a. When an acid is 10% ionized (or a base is 90% ionized), the pH is one unit below the pK_a. When an acid is 90% ionized (or a base is 10% ionized), the pH is one unit above the pK_a. Again, when an acid is 1% ionized, the pH is two units below the pK_a, and when it is $0\cdot 1\%$ ionized, the pH is three units below the pK_a, and so on. From these data it is easy to visualize the shape of the neutralization curve of an acid (or base), provided that it is not too weak. Such a curve is shown in Fig. 1.1, and is sigmoid in shape.

7

TABLE 1.1

Interconversion of K_a and pK_a

To convert K_a to pK_a, take the logarithm of the constant and subtract this from zero. For example, acetic acid has the ionization constant $1·75 \times 10^{-5}$; the logarithm ($\overline{5}·2430$) subtracted from 0 gives 4·7570, which is the pK_a. Bases, when expressed as pK_a, are converted in exactly the same way.

To convert pK_a to K_a, subtract the pK_a from zero, and then take the antilogarithm of the figure obtained.

Practice may be had with the following examples, covering up one column at a time.

	pK_a (20°)	K_a
Benzoic acid	4·12	$7·6 \times 10^{-5}$
p-Nitroaniline	1·01	$9·8 \times 10^{-2}$
Ammonia	9·36	$4·4 \times 10^{-10}$
p-Cresol	10·14	$7·2 \times 10^{-11}$
Methylamine	10·81	$1·5 \times 10^{-11}$

When bases are expressed as K_b, as in the older literature, it is convenient to convert them first to pK_b (using the same procedure as for pK_a) and then to convert to pK_a by subtracting the result from 14·17 (at 20°), or 14·00 (at 25°). For example, one reported pK_b value for ammonia is $1·5 \times 10^{-5}$ (at 20°). The logarithm of this is $\overline{5}·1761$. This, subtracted from zero, gives 4·8239. Subtracting 4·82 from 14·17 gives 9·35 which is the pK_a at 20°.

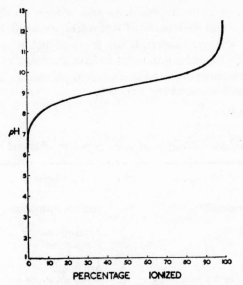

Fig. 1.1. Typical curve obtained in the potentiometric titration of an acid (boric acid, $pK_a = 9.2$ at 20°)

How to calculate the percentage ionized

Appendix IV (p. 173) shows the percentage (of an acid or base) that is ionized at various values of pH and pK_a. These figures were calculated from equation (1.9) for bases, and equation (1.10) for acids.

$$\% \text{ Ionized} = \frac{100}{1 + \text{antilog (pH} - pK_a)} \tag{1.9}$$

$$\% \text{ Ionized} = \frac{100}{1 + \text{antilog (} pK_a - \text{pH)}} \tag{1.10}$$

It may be deduced from these equations, and also from Fig. 1.1, and Appendix IV, that a small change in pH can make a large change in the percentage ionized. This is particularly significant if the values of pH and pK lie close together, as they do near the point of half-neutralization.

9

Table 1·2 gives the approximate pKs of some common acids and bases. Acids and bases of equivalent strengths have been placed opposite one another. It will prove advantageous to commit this table to memory in order to have a number of reference points for assessing the significance of new pK values. More complete data will be found in Chapter 8.

TABLE 1.2

Approximate strengths of some common acids and bases

Acids	pK_a	Bases	pK_a
Hydrochloric acid*		Sodium hydroxide*	
	1		13
Oxalic acid	2	Acetamidine	12
	3	Ethylamine	11
	4		10
Acetic acid	5	Ammonia	9
Carbonic acid	6	Many alkaloids	8
	7		7
	8		6
Hydrocyanic acid, boric acid	9	Aniline, pyridine	5
Phenol	10		4
	11		3
	12		2
Sucrose	13	*p*-Nitroaniline	1

* Fully ionized, pK_a not easily measurable.

Methods available for determining ionization constants

By far the most convenient method for the determination of ionization constants is *potentiometric titration*. This is described in detail in Chapter 2 (some refinements are discussed in Chapter 3). Potentiometric titration requires two electrodes: glass and calomel electrodes form the most serviceable pair. The use of a hydrogen electrode in place of the glass electrode is not recommended for general use: it is more troublesome, and has often given wrong values due to hydrogenation of the substance being determined. Apart from its use as a primary standard, the principal value of the hydrogen electrode is in determining the ionization constants of very weak acids or very strong bases, particularly substances with a pK_a of 11 or more (see p. 49). Between pH 12 and 14, the glass electrode is inaccurate. A silver electrode is preferred by some to the calomel electrode. Quinhydrone and antimony electrodes are now seldom used.

The use of *indicators* instead of electrodes to measure ionization constants by observing pH changes during titration is a form of potentiometry. This is a tedious method which can give good results in practised hands,* but is not now so much used as formerly. A special use of this method is to define solutions of known acidity function (see p. 71).

Whereas potentiometry enables an ionization constant to be determined in 20 minutes, ultraviolet *spectrophotometry* usually requires the greater part of a working day. Nevertheless it is particularly suitable for sparingly soluble substances, and also for work at very high and very low pH values which are beyond the range of the glass electrode. It can be used only for substances which absorb ultraviolet or visible light, and the relevant ionic species must show absorption maxima at different wavelengths. Spectrophotometry is related to potentiometry in that the spectra are determined in buffers whose pH values are determined by potentiometry. Whereas potentiometric determination of an ionization constant measures the hydrogen ions not bound by the unknown, the spectrometric method measures the spectral shift produced when the unknown binds hydrogen ions. The spectrophotometric method is explained in Chapter 4. *Raman spectra* and *nuclear magnetic resonance* permit the determination of the ionization constants of such strong acids as nitric and trifluoroacetic acids.†

The determination of ionization constants by *conductimetry* takes somewhat longer than by potentiometry. It is a less versatile method but it is specially useful for very weak acids (i.e. for those

---

* For an example of this method see KOLTHOFF, *Biochem. Zeitschr.*, 1925, **162**, 289.
† REDLICH and HOOD, *Disc. Farad. Soc.*, 1957, **24**, 87.

with a pK_a greater than 12). Most of the ionization constants determined before 1930 were found by conductimetry, but many of these old values are inaccurate. Nevertheless the method is capable of giving highly accurate results if sufficient care is taken. The conductimetric method is explained in Chapter 5.

Another method, discussed in Chapter 6, is determination of the *increase in aqueous solubility* of the unknown at various pH values. This is not so accurate a method as potentiometry, spectrophotometry and conductimetry, but it is useful in those cases, fortunately rare, where a substance (*a*) is too insoluble in water for potentiometry or conductimetry, and (*b*) has no useful ultraviolet spectra. *The catalysis of hydrolysis* of an ester, disaccharide or glucoside, as a measure of ionization constants, has only historical interest. Sometimes it led to grossly erroneous results.

The degree of precision to be aimed at

When a set of results has been obtained, the investigator must decide quickly whether they are good enough for his purpose, or whether the determination should be repeated with some change in conditions. In our experience, a set of results (from a single determination) that has a wide scatter, has usually turned out to be even more inaccurate than it appears to be. Thus a pK_a of $7 \cdot 83 \pm 0 \cdot 2$ (where $\pm 0 \cdot 2$ is the scatter or spread) is as likely to lie outside the range $7 \cdot 63$ to $8 \cdot 03$ as in it. Thus this degree of precision ($\pm 0 \cdot 2$) is not sufficient for accuracy. At the other extreme, an investigator attempting to obtain an ionization constant with less scatter than $\pm 0 \cdot 01$ may have to spend many weeks or months on determinations, and this would only be justified if he were trying to establish an international standard for some calibration purpose.

Obviously a middle way must exist. The majority of readers of this book will want to obtain trustworthy values, ones that can be repeated throughout the scientific world. At the same time they will usually want to obtain these values with reasonable speed. From experience we think that *no more scatter than 0·06 in a pK_a value should be allowed* for a set of readings in any one estimation. We shall leave the definition of a 'set' until each technique is discussed, because it differs for each technique.

Scatter is calculated by taking antilogarithms of each pK_a value in a set, averaging these, and writing down the logarithm of the average as the pK_a. The largest deviation between this value and any value in the set is then written after the pK_a as its scatter. Thus if the average is found to be 3·93, and the nine values of the set (of which it is an average) were respectively 3·91, 3·91, 3·93, 3·95, 3·94, 3·96, 3·97, 3·94, 3·91, then the value 3·97 has the largest deviation, namely 0·04, and so the scatter is recorded as ±0·04 (or +0·04 and −0·02), and the complete pK_a is reported as 3·93 ± 0·04.

The following illustrates the error of averaging logarithms instead of first converting the values to antilogarithms. Addition of two pK_a values, say 2·10 and 2·90, and division of the sum by two gives 2·50 which is wrong, because it is not a mean but a square root! Instead, the pK_a values should be converted to their antilogarithms (126 + 794): these are added and the sum is divided by two, giving 460. The logarithm of 460 is 2·66, and this is the correct average.

Some authors like to report their constants with a 'probable error' instead of a scatter. The use of probable error suggests a smaller deviation than is the case, and withholds useful information from the reader who usually wants to know the maximal deviation. The probable error is obtained by subtracting the average pK_a from each value in the set without attention to sign. The sum (Σ) of these deviations is then multiplied by 3 and divided by the product of the number of values in a set and the square root of this number. Thus, in the example given above, 3·93 is subtracted from each of the nine values: the differences added without regard to sign give $\Sigma = 0·17$. The probable error is then:

$$\frac{3 \times 0·17}{9\sqrt{9}} \quad \text{or} \quad \frac{0·51}{27} \quad \text{or} \quad 0·02$$

The 'order of accuracy', which is the probable error divided by the average value, provides an even smaller number, but again this information is not so helpful to readers as the scatter. The number of readings in a set must be reported for the full significance of the scatter to be apparent.

The effect of temperature on ionization constants

Ionization constants vary with temperature, the correlation curve is usually a parabola with a rather flat maximum. For many acids, including all carboxylic acids, this maximum is near 20–25°, and hence the ionization constants of such substances can be determined without refined temperature control. Thus the first pK_a of citric acid lies between 4·44 and 4·47 throughout the range 12·5° to 91°. Phenol, however, becomes stronger by 0·012 unit of pK_a for each degree rise in temperature. Some inorganic acids, like phosphoric acid, are temperature-insensitive, whereas boric acid becomes stronger by about 0·006 unit per °C.

Nitrogenous bases are temperature-sensitive, becoming weaker as the temperature is increased. Thus the pK_a of aniline is 4·66 at 20°, but only 4·52 at 30°. The temperature effect is much greater with stronger than with weaker bases. The temperature coefficients of a number of bases (including alklylamines, aniline and pyridine) have been recorded in water between 19° and 30° and are summarized in Table 1·3. This table not only illustrates the dependence of the magnitude of the coefficient on that of the

TABLE 1.3

Temperature coefficients for nitrogenous bases between 0° and 40°

If the pK_a is	subtract for each °C rise	If the pK_a is	subtract for each °C rise
3·3	0·011	6·6	0·017
4·2	0·013	7·5	0·018
4·6	0·014	9·0	0·020
5·0	0·015	10·0	0·021
5·8	0·016	11·0	0·022

From HALL and SPRINKLE, *J. Amer. Chem. Soc.*, 1932, **54**, 3469.

pK_a, but also enables rough conversion of constants from one temperature to another.

From the above, it is evident that good temperature control is required in the standardization of a potentiometer with borax buffer, and also in the determination of the ionization constants of all bases and many acids.

2

Determination of Ionization Constants
by Potentiometric Titration
using a glass electrode

Potentiometry, because it is so economical of time, is usually the best choice in determining ionization constants. The apparatus described in this chapter is based on the familiar potentiometer assembly commonly referred to as a 'pH set'. If used with care, this apparatus can be made to give acceptable results. More accurate results can be obtained with a vibrating-reed electrometer, as described in Chapter 3, a piece of apparatus which is about four times more expensive.

The *hydrogen electrode* is the ultimate standard to which all determinations of pH are referred. The solution to be measured is saturated with hydrogen, and is confined in an atmosphere of this gas. The electrode consists of finely divided platinum (adhering to a platinum plate) which reversibly converts hydrogen gas into hydrogen ions, thus:

$$H_2 \rightleftharpoons 2H^+ + 2\varepsilon \qquad (2.1)$$

The metal plate takes up the free charge (indicated above by the two electrons, 2ε) from the solution until the electric potential between the plate and the solution has built up so as to prevent further change. This potential is a measure of the tendency of the gas to split into ions and so pass into the solution. If the hydrogen gas is at a pressure of one atmosphere and the potential of the electrode is E (in volts), then

$$E = -\frac{RT}{F} \ln \{H^+\} \qquad (2.2)$$

where T is the absolute temperature, R the gas constant and F the Faraday. To measure this potential, the platinum plate is connected to the measuring instrument, which is essentially a potentiometer plus a high resistance galvanometer, and the circuit is completed through a second electrode of constant potential, usually a calomel half-cell. The pH of the unknown solution is calculated from (2.3).

$$- \log_{10} \{H^+\} = pH = \frac{E_o - E_c}{0 \cdot 0591} \text{ at } 25° \qquad (2.3)$$

where E_o is the observed potential and E_c is the potential of the calomel electrode under the experimental conditions.

Apparatus for general use

The use of the hydrogen electrode to determine ionization constants is described on p. 49. This electrode is rather inconvenient to use because it is easily poisoned, and it often chemically alters the substance being measured.

A more convenient electrode has largely replaced the hydrogen electrode in commercial potentiometric apparatus. This, the *glass electrode*, consists of a thin-walled bulb of soft glass containing hydrochloric acid into which a small silver electrode dips. The circuit is completed with a calomel or silver chloride half-cell. Essentially, the potential across a glass membrane is proportional to the pH of the solution. However when a high ratio of sodium to hydrogen ions exists, sodium ions penetrate the membrane and give a false reading. For this reason, potassium hydroxide is preferred to sodium hydroxide in potentiometric titrations, because a higher ratio of potassium to hydrogen ions can exist before accuracy is affected. Tetraethylammonium hydroxide gives less error than potassium hydroxide, but it is too unstable in solution for convenient use.*

---

* When determining the pKa values of strong organic bases, the errors arising from inorganic cations can be avoided by simply measuring pH values after the addition of an equivalent of hydrochloric acid to the free base in ten equal portions (SEARLES, TAMRES, BLOCK and QUARTERMAN, *J. Amer. Chem. Soc.*, 1956, **78**, 4917).

The potential generated by the hydrogen ions in the solution is measured by an electronic potentiometer assembly which is based on a thermionic valve. The relationship between the potential of the glass electrode and the pH of the solution has the general form of equation (2.3), but involves terms which can change daily through asymmetry potentials and other variable effects. Hence this electrode cannot be used as a primary standard, but it does provide a very convenient way of comparing the pH of a series of solutions. To serve in this way, it is calibrated before and after use with a pair of known buffers, the pH of one of which must lie near to the pH region to be measured.

Not every make of pH set is suitable for potentiometric titration, because the titration technique requires that the instrument should hold its reference potential for a period at least as long as is necessary to determine the pK_a. A pH set may be tested for suitability by connecting it to accumulators and earth (through the three appropriate terminals) and leaving it switched on for half an hour. After checking against the inbuilt standard cell, until there is no more drift, the circuit should be balanced with the glass and calomel electrodes immersed in 0·05M-potassium hydrogen phthalate, the potentiometer dial being set to pH 4·00. One hour later, it should not be necessary to change the potentiometer by more than 0·01 of a pH unit to re-establish balance. (If the instrument is only occasionally unsteady, a possible fault is that the batteries are overcharged or undercharged.) A knock, or some vibration, can upset the balance of a pH set by varying the distance between the grid and filament of the valve. Hence, for titrations, the set is conveniently placed on a sponge-rubber pad on a sturdy bench in a small, quiet room. Although several makes of pH set have proved suitable for titrations, our own preference is for the Cambridge Bench Pattern pH meter, which is calibrated in 0·02 unit. Another highly stable, but more expensive, set is the Radiometer Company's Model pH-M4 which is calibrated in 0·01 unit, transistorized, and operated by dry cells. Mains-operated pH sets are usually not steady enough for titration work and the few which are reliable are also expensive. An example of the better class of mains-operated set is the Universal pH meter, model 22, made by the Radiometer Company in Copenhagen. It has no zero drift and requires no warming up, but the scale is calibrated in rather large units (0·05 pH). Automatic titration devices, if without differentiating circuits, are to be avoided because they remove human control where it is most needed to ensure accurate work.

For a pair of electrodes we recommend one calomel electrode* (sintered plug type) and one glass electrode. The latter should be purchased with a coaxially shielded lead which avoids capacity effects. The leads on each electrode should be about one metre long. The glass electrode should be of the common kind which is unattacked by acid. The working life of such an electrode may turn out to be about three months. Whether it is fit for use may be determined as follows. Immerse it in 0·05M-potassium hydrogen phthalate and adjust the potentiometer dial to pH 4·00. Then wash it and immerse it in 0·05M-sodium borate (borax): the instrument should now balance at the pH given in Appendix III (e.g. pH 9·23 at 20°) *without any further adjustment*. If the instrument requires more adjustment than ±0·01 before coming to balance in borate buffer at the specified pH, the electrode must be rejected.

It is also possible to obtain special electrodes for the region above pH 12. These have diminished permeability to potassium ions but are injuriously affected by acid. All those with which we have had experience have lost sensitivity after a little use, in spite of careful treatment. Such electrodes may be tested, after standardization with phthalate and borate buffers as above, by immersion in 0·01M-trisodium phosphate.† If the *special* glass electrode is in good condition, it should record a pH that falls less short of the correct pH (11·90 at 20° and 11·72 at 25°) than that simultaneously recorded by a phthalate and borate-standardized *ordinary* glass electrode immersed alongside it.

---

* The calomel electrode is more reproducible than the silver chloride electrode (HILL and IVES, *J. Chem. Soc.*, 1951, 305) which is affected by oxygen in acidic solution and is dissolved by amines.
† Na_2HPO_4 (1·419 g.) and 0·1N-NaOH (100 ml.) in 1 litre of water.

When not in use, all electrodes must be scrupulously cared for according to the manufacturer's instructions.

The titration is conveniently carried out in tall beakers, of which 50 ml. and 100 ml. sizes are useful. The beaker is closed with a cork bung bored with five holes, of which two are for the electrodes, one is for the nitrogen inlet, one for the thermometer, and one is to admit the tip of a burette or micrometer syringe. The electrodes should not make too tight a fit in the cork and are secured by two spring clips (e.g. Terry clips) to a miniature retort stand. The electrodes are connected by their shielded leads to the terminals of the pH set, and the retort stand is earthed by another wire. This arrangement is shown in Fig. 2.1.

Stirring is best accomplished by a slow stream of nitrogen bubbles. The gas is best introduced under the surface of the solution to be titrated. Its flow should be stopped during readings if it is found to interfere with them. Too fast a flow will cause some loss of solution as spray.

The nitrogen should be purified by first bubbling through Fieser's solution which is made by dissolving sodium dithionite (16 g.), sodium anthraquinone-2-sulphonate (0·8 g.), and sodium hydroxide (15 g.) in water (100 ml.). Freed from oxygen and carbon dioxide in this way, the nitrogen should next be freed from alkaline spray by bubbling through a little water.

The titrant, acid or alkali, may be delivered from a burette or from a micrometer syringe. Use of the latter, which has a vernier scale, is essential if the total volume to be delivered is small. If a burette is used for alkali the contents can be protected from entry of carbon dioxide as shown in Fig. 2.2 (the guard tube is normally closed with a rubber bung). We use the 'Agla' micrometer syringe (Burroughs, Wellcome & Co.) with the bent glass needles, as supplied. It is convenient to have two of these syringes, one for acid and one for alkali. A certain deftness must be acquired in filling and using the alkali syringe to minimize contact with carbon dioxide from the air.

As has been explained above, good temperature control is essential for meaningful results. The room used for titrations

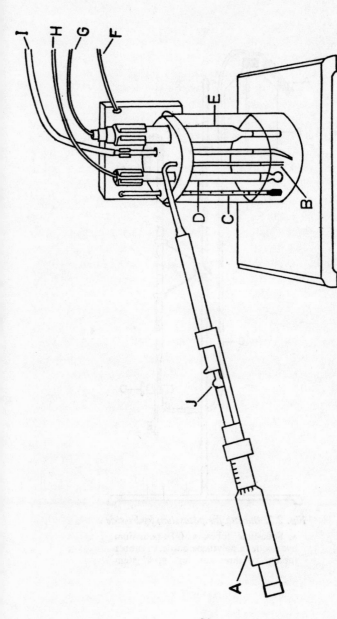

Fig. 2.1. Standard titration apparatus

A, Vernier micrometer (of syringe). B, Glass needle (of syringe). C, Thermometer. D, Glass electrode. E, Calomel electrode. F, Connexion to earth. G, Lead to positive terminal of pH set. H, Shielded lead to negative terminal. I, Inlet for nitrogen. J, Plunger of syringe

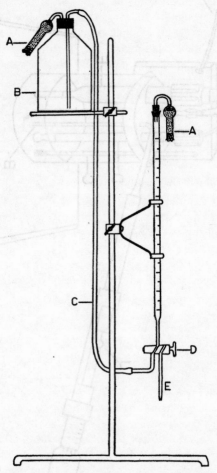

Fig. 2.2. Burette for potassium hydroxide
A, Soda-lime tubes. B, 0·1N-potassium
hydroxide in polythene bottle. C, rubber
tubing. D, three-way tap. E, 6″ stem

22

should be free from draughts and should not vary much in temperature throughout the day. This room's prevailing temperature should not be above that designated for the titrations (see below) and the relative humidity should be between 20 and 60%. In particular, the apparatus should be situated where no shaft of sunlight can fall on it at any time during the day. The titration vessel should stand in a bath of water which is maintained at the temperature required for the titration. The maintenance of this temperature may be either automatic or manual (e.g. by addition of hot or cold water).

Preparation of solutions

Solutions must be made in water that has been freed from carbon dioxide if alkali is the titrant. The ion-free water obtained by running distilled water through an ion-exchange column is suitable if the conductivity is sufficiently low (10^{-5} reciprocal ohms). Alternatively, 'boiled-out water' can be made by boiling distilled water vigorously for five minutes, closing the vessel with a well-cleaned rubber bung, and cooling: such water is also oxygen-free and is useful for titrating readily oxidized substances. The substances to be titrated are most conveniently dissolved by magnetic stirring, which is accomplished by inserting a small, plastic-coated iron bar in the titration vessel which is then stood on the usual magnetic flux stand. The electrodes should not be placed in the vessel until all the substance is dissolved. Magnetic stirring is best replaced by nitrogen gas stirring during the titration (see above), but the plastic-coated rod may be left in place.

If heating is used to aid dissolution, the solution must be cooled to the designated titrating temperature, or below that, before the electrodes are immersed in it. Most glass electrodes show a hysteresis effect on cooling and will not record a steady pH for some time after being cooled.* There is, fortunately, no hysteresis on warming. If the temperature of the titrating room cannot be maintained at, or below, the temperature designated for titrations,

---

* IRVING and WILLIAMS, *J. Chem. Soc.*, 1950, 2890.

the glass electrode should be stored in a thermostat, at the designated temperature.

Preparation of carbonate-free potassium hydroxide

Although it is easier to obtain carbonate-free sodium hydroxide than potassium hydroxide, the latter is invariably used as the alkali in potentiometric titrations because it gives rise to less electrode error in alkaline solutions. The commercial sticks of potassium hydroxide usually have all the carbonate on the outside. Hence it is possible to wash a weighed amount of potassium hydroxide (the fused, 15% hydrated sticks), to titrate these washings (which are then rejected), and hence find how much water to add to the residue to make slightly stronger than decinormal potassium hydroxide. A further titration and dilution should give exactly 0·100N-KOH. These operations should be conducted in some easily contrived apparatus entirely out of contact with the carbon dioxide of the air. The absence of carbonate is usually confirmed by potentiometric titration of the amino-acid histidine, for whose pK_a of 6·08 no agreeing set of nine values can be obtained in the presence of a disturbing amount of carbon dioxide. We do not highly recommend the above preparation because some batches of potassium hydroxide sticks have minute fissures which cause the potassium carbonate to interpenetrate so that it cannot be washed off. The following ion-exchange methods is preferable.[*]

In summary, barium hydroxide is added to a solution of commercial potassium hydroxide (analytical grade). The precipitate of barium carbonate is allowed to settle and the excess barium ions removed by passing the solutions through a column of ion-exchange resin (Amberlite IR 120) which is quantitatively in the potassium form: RSO_3K (R is the matrix of the resin). The eluate is a solution of pure potassium hydroxide free from carbonate.

(a) Precipitation of carbonate: A.R. potassium hydroxide (14 g.) is dissolved in ion-free water (about 1·5 litres), and A.R. barium hydroxide (3 g.) is added. The suspension is shaken for 15 minutes in a conical flask sealed with a rubber stopper through which a glass

---

[*] Based on that of ARMSTRONG, *Chem. and Ind.*, 1955, 1405.

tube protrudes, by 2 inches, into the flask. The flask is inverted and allowed to stand overnight so that the precipitate of barium carbonate settles below the level of the outlet tube.

(*b*) Preparation of the resin: Amberlite resin IR 120H (50 ml. analytical grade) is made into a slurry with water and poured into a column fitted with a three-way double oblique bore stopcock. The resin is backwashed with N-HCl (1 litre) and then with water (*ca.* 1·5 litres) to remove excess acid. Next, 0·2N-potassium chloride solution (about 1·5 litres) is passed through the column from the top until the pH values of the entrant and eluate solutions are identical (about 1·3 litres are required). The potassium chloride solution is then allowed to remain in contact with the resin for a further hour and the remaining 200 ml. is then passed through. This ensures that the resin is quantitatively in the potassium form. The excess potassium chloride solution is removed by downwashing the column with ion-free water until 100 ml. of eluate gives no turbidity with acidified silver nitrate solution (approximately 1·8 litres of water is required). To ensure that the water flowing through the resin is carbonate-free, the washing is carried out in an inert atmosphere using the arrangement shown in Fig. 2.3. The wash water is discarded.

(*c*) Purification of the carbonate-free potassium hydroxide solution containing barium ions: The conical flask containing the impure potassium hydroxide is connected to the top of the column and the solution passed through the column. The first 100 ml. is rejected and the remainder passed through the polythene tube into a nitrogen-filled 2-litre polythene bottle previously calibrated in 100 ml. division and fitted with a soda-lime guard tube. When the flow from the conical flask ceases, a calibrated 500-ml. polythene bottle fitted with a polythene syphon tube and soda-lime guard tube and containing ion-free water is attached to the top of the column. The resin is then washed with water (200 ml.) and the eluate is combined with the potassium hydroxide solution in the polythene bottle. The tube connecting the column to the polythene bottle is sealed with a screw-clip and then disconnected from the column. Nitrogen is bubbled through the

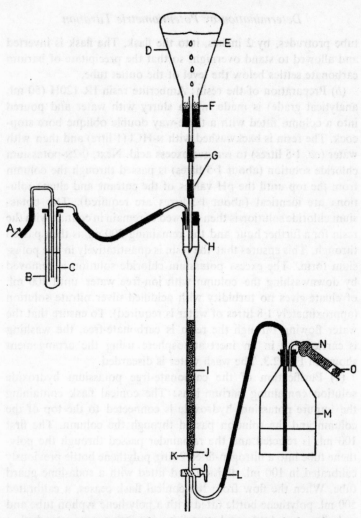

Fig. 2.3. Preparation of carbonate-free potassium hydroxide

A, Inlet for nitrogen. B, Pressure regulator, Pregl's type with loosely-fitting bung (Gallenkamp Cat. No. 13607/1). C, N-Potassium hydroxide (as CO_2 trap). D, Conical flask (2 litre). E, Potassium and barium hydroxides. F, Precipitated barium carbonate. G, Polythene tubing, suitable for clamping. H, End ground to 45°. I, Amberlite resin (IR 120) as potassium form. J, Glass bead. K, Slight constriction. L, Polythene tubing to base of polythene bottle. M, Polythene bottle (2·2 litres capacity). N, Soda lime. O, Cotton-wool plug

potassium hydroxide solution for 10 minutes with occasional swirling to ensure a homogeneous solution. The bottle is then connected to a 50-ml. burette and the potassium hydroxide solution is standardized against A.R. potassium hydrogen phthalate (dried 1 hr. at 120°) using phenolphthalein as indicator. The volume in the bottle is adjusted by further small additions of ion-free water until the potassium hydroxide solution is exactly 0·1000N, the normality being checked after each addition. The yield is about 2 litres. We find that the carbonate content, determined on 800 ml. by a standardized micro-gravimetric method (the increase in weight of soda-lime after the liberation of CO_2 by excess acid), is less than 1 p.p.m.

The choice of concentrations for titration

We recommend that substances be titrated at 0·01M concentration wherever solubility permits. At this concentration, activity effects are usually small (see p. 60). However concentrations up to 0·1M may be used if activity corrections, as on p. 59, are carried out.

The limits of pK_a determinable accurately with the glass electrode are, in our experience, 1·25 to 11·0, but the hydrogen electrode (p. 49) has been used up to pK_a 13·65.*

Accurate results cannot be expected if the pK_a is less than the negative logarithm of the concentration (thus, 0·01M is unsuitable for a pK_a less than 2).

Because of poor solubility, it may be desired to titrate a solution more dilute than 0·01M. The rule of the negative logarithm of the dilution will indicate, after a preliminary titration, if reliable results could be expected at such a dilution. Where doubt exists, the pH values arising during the titration of a similar volume of water should be compared with the pH values arising during the dubious titration to see if the two series of figures differ significantly. If it is desired to titrate solutions more dilute than 0·001M,

---

* HALL and SPRINKLE, *J. Amer. Chem. Soc.*, 1932, **54**, 3469; THAMSEN, *Acta Chem. Scand.*, 1952, **6**, 270.

recourse should be had to more sensitive apparatus (see Chapter 3, p. 47).

The ionic strength of a 0·01M solution of a univalent substance, when half neutralized, is 0·005. Some workers like to titrate all solutions 'at constant ionic strength', usually by making them 0·1M in potassium chloride. However this should not be done when using the methods described in this chapter which avoid activity calculations (they also avoid corrections for liquid junction potentials). As an indication of the degree of accuracy obtainable, 0·01M-acetic acid was titrated at 20° and gave pK_a 4·74 ± 0·03. This can be compared with the thermodynamic pK_a (4·7560) which was obtained* by using every possible refinement of technique and calculations.

Details of the titration method

The temperature dial on the pH apparatus is to be set to the required temperature. Next, the glass electrode is standardized on phthalate *and* borate buffers as described on p. 19.† A solution of the substance is prepared as described on p. 23, at a concentration suggested by the considerations discussed on p. 27. The solution is brought to the required temperature, and stirring by a slow stream of nitrogen (see p. 20) is begun. The pH is read. The titrant is then added in ten equal portions, each a tenth of an equivalent, and the pH is recorded as soon as equilibrium is reached after each addition. No credence can be given to pKs which are reported as 'the pH recorded at half neutralization'.

When the titration is complete, the electrodes are at once washed, and placed in either phthalate, borate or trisodium phosphate buffer (choosing the buffer which is nearer to the pK found). If its pH is not reproduced to ±0·02 *without adjustment of the set*, the titration results must be discarded. If the potential repeatedly strays in this way during a titration, one of the electrodes may be faulty, the temperature may not be as steady as is supposed, or the

---

* HARNED and EHLERS, *J. Amer. Chem. Soc.*, 1932, **54**, 1350.
† For an expected pK_a higher than 10·5, standardization on borate and sodium tri-phosphate (p. 19) is advised.

electronic valve may be too easily disturbed by vibrations (see p. 18).

Dilution of the solution by the titrant causes little error provided (*a*) that the titrant is at least ten times as concentrated as the substance being titrated and (*b*) that the concentration on which calculations are based is reached at the mid-point of the titration as in Tables 2.1 and 2.2. By using a titrant which is 100 times as concentrated as the substance, the latter can be prepared for titration in the concentration on which calculations are based, as in Table 2.3. If, however, it is desired to correct for the dilution caused by the water introduced by the titrant, an adjustment can be made as follows.

Insert, into the table, an extra column giving the total concentration of material being titrated, regardless of species. For example, in Table 2.2, this column (*2a*) would come between columns 2 and 3, and the figures in it would progressively decline according to the progressive dilution caused by the titrant, passing through 0·01 at 2·5 ml. The figures for columns 3 and 4 should next be adjusted so that, on every line, they add up to the value found in column *2a*. The rest of the table remains as before.

The most difficult titrations with the glass electrode are those of substances with pK_a of 11 or higher. The following sources of error can contribute to an inaccurate result,

(*a*) Standardization of the electrode at a pH no higher than that of borate buffer (about pH 9·2) which is too far from the pH region covered in the titration,

(*b*) The nature of the glass electrode which becomes more and more porous to potassium ions as the ratio K^+/H^+ increases,

(*c*) A minute but significant amount of carbon dioxide may enter from the air even when great care is taken to exclude it.

Hence we recommend that potentiometry with the glass electrode be not used for substances of pK_a more than 11, or, above pH 11, for solutions diluter than 0·01M. Potentiometry with the hydrogen electrode (p. 49), spectrophotometry (Chapter 4) and conduct-imetry (Chapter 5), are more suited to the high pK_a region.

Derivation and choice of equations for calculating pK_a

If the pH remains between 4 and 10 when a 0·01M solution is being titrated, only the very simple calculations shown in Table 2.1 (p. 33) need be carried out. The expression $[AH]/[A^-]$ in column 6 occupies a key position and is derived from equation (1.3). The figures in column 6 are independent of the dilution: they are few in number and it is very useful to commit them to memory. Thus, in titrations of this simple kind, only columns 1, 2, 6 and 7 need appear in the practical notebook, and column 6 is always the same.

Often, however, the pH range of a 0·01M titration falls outside the limits pH 4–10. Even in Table 2.1, the last usable reading (pH 10·14) falls outside this range. If this value is corrected for hydroxyl ion concentration as in Table 2.4, the corresponding pK_a value rises from 9·19 to 9·23, and the final result is sharpened from 9·25 $\pm$ 0·06 to 9·26 $\pm$ 0·03.

If the solution being titrated is more dilute, the pH must remain between narrower values throughout the titration if such corrections are to be avoided. Thus for a 0·001M solution, the pH must remain between 5 and 9.

The necessity for allowing for hydrogen ion (and hydroxyl ion) concentrations, should either become significantly large, arises from the fact that all solutions are electrically neutral. Hence the sum of all positive charges must equal the sum of all negative charges, thus,

$$[A^-] + [OH^-] = [K^+] + [H^+] \qquad (2.4, a)$$

Because all salts are completely ionized, $[K^+]$ equals the concentration of potassium hydroxide (after allowing for dilution by the solution). Hence

$$[A^-] = [KOH] - [OH^-] + [H^+] \qquad (2.4, b)$$

[Y], the total concentration of acid taken, is present in two forms,

A⁻ and HA, hence,

$$[Y] = [A^-] + [HA], \qquad (2.4, c)$$

By combining (2.4, *b* and *c*), we get:

$$[HA] = [Y] - [KOH] + [OH^-] - [H^+] \qquad (2.4, d)$$

When, as in column 4 of Table 2.2, we take $[A^-]$ as equal to $[KOH]$, we are assuming that $[H^+]$ and $[OH^-]$ are negligible by comparison, and speak of 'the stoicheiometric concentration'. This approximation cannot be used in more strongly alkaline or acidic regions. Thus $[A^-]$ is $[KOH] + [H^+]$ in the acidic region, or $[KOH] - [OH^-]$ in the alkaline region (from equation 2.4, *b*). Likewise the real concentration of $[HA]$ is $[Y] - [KOH] - [H^+]$ in the acidic region, or $[Y] - [KOH] + [OH^-]$ in the alkaline region. This small amount of extra calculation refines the results in a very gratifying way. The calculation of $[H^+]$ and $[OH^-]$ from the pH reading is explained in Appendix I.

The calculation of the ionization constant of a base follows similarly, from equation (1.6). When the results lie between pH 4 and 10 (for a 0·01M solution), hydrogen ion and hydroxyl ion corrections can be neglected and column 6 is headed simply $[B]/[BH^+]$, as in Table 2.5. For results below pH 4, this heading is changed to $[B] + [H^+]/[BH^+] - [H^+]$ as in Table 2.6. Similarly, above pH 10, the heading to column 6 becomes $[B] - [OH^-]/[BH^+] + [OH^-]$, as in Table 2.7.

Some typical titrations (worked examples)

These worked examples cover the commoner types of potentiometric titration and show how the results are best tabulated.

Table 2.1. shows the titration of 0·01M boric acid, and is typical of a titration not requiring hydrogen ion or hydroxyl ion corrections (see immediately above). Actually the last value in the set does rise above pH 10 and the pK_a calculated from it is improved by a correction as explained on p. 30.

Table 2.2 (benzoic acid) is typical of a titration requiring

31

correction for *hydrogen* ions. Table 2.3, the titration of 0·01M-sodium benzoate with a strong acid, is virtually the same titration as in Table 2.2, but approached from the opposite direction. Comparison of the pair of Tables 2.2 and 2.3 will show how any titration can be tackled from alternative directions without substantial changes in the calculations. Table 2.4, the titration of *p*-cresol, provides an example of an acid requiring correction for *hydroxyl* ions.

In Table 2.5 the much used buffer 'Tris' is titrated as an example of a base not requiring correction. Table 2.6 gives an example (*p*-chloroaniline) of a base requiring correction for *hydrogen* ions. Table 2.7 shows the titration of glycine, from the zwitterion $H_3N^+.CH_2CO_2^-$ to the anion $H_2N.CH_2CO_2^-$. Zwitterions will be discussed in Chapter 7, and it may be sufficient now to say that Table 2.7 shows the titration of an amino-group from its cation to the neutral form. This example illustrates correction for *hydroxyl* ions in the titration of a base.

Precision and accuracy. Checking the precision obtained

Although a result can be precise (i.e. contained within a narrow spread) without being accurate (i.e. true), the reverse is not the case. Hence it is desirable to see that the average of all values, in a set of nine values, falls within a spread of ± 0.06 (see p. 12). With care and experience, this scatter can be greatly reduced as is evident from Tables 2.2 to 2.7 which are records of recent titrations in our laboratories. The commonest causes of too large a spread are (*a*) the presence of impurities in the substance being titrated, and (*b*) small inaccuracies in adding the titrant (see below under 'common sources of error'). Such errors often are most evident in the first or ninth value of a set, leaving the inner seven values acceptably close.

TABLE 2.1

Determination of the ionization constant of a monobasic acid requiring no correction for hydrogen or hydroxyl ions

Substance: Boric acid. $H_3BO_3 = 61.84$. *Temperature:* 20°
Concentration: 0·01M at half neutralization. Boric acid (0·0309 g.), dried overnight in a vacuum desiccator ($CaCl_2$, 20 mm., 20°), was dissolved in 47·5 ml. of boiled-out water.

1	2	3	4	5	6	7
		Stoicheiometric concentrations*				
Titrant 0·1N-KOH	Potentio-meter reading	Species with hydrogen ion	Species without hydrogen ion	$\dfrac{[HA]}{[A^-]}$	log of column 5	pK_a (= pH + column 6)
ml.	pH	[HA]	[A⁻]			
0	6·16	0·010	0			
0·5	8·34	0·009	0·001	9/1	0·95	9·29
1·0	8·68	0·008	0·002	8/2	0·60	9·28
1·5	8·89	0·007	0·003	7/3	0·37	9·26
2·0	9·07	0·006	0·004	6/4	0·18	9·25
2·5	9·26	0·005	0·005	5/5	0	9·26
3·0	9·43	0·004	0·006	4/6	−0·18	9·25
3·5	9·62	0·003	0·007	3/7	−0·37	9·25
4·0	9·84	0·002	0·008	2/8	−0·60	9·24
4·5	10·14	0·001	0·009	1/9	−0·95	9·19
5·0	10·56	0	0·010			

Result: $pK_a = 9.25$ (± 0.06) at 0·01M and 20° (using all nine values in the set). If the pH 10·14 reading is corrected for [OH⁻], as in Table 2.4, the value 9·19 becomes 9·23 and the final result is sharpened to 9.26 ± 0.03.

* The stoicheiometric concentrations are those which would be present if each portion of the alkali reacted with its equivalent of the acid (p. 31).

TABLE 2.2

Determination of the ionization constant of a monobasic acid requiring correction for the concentration of hydrogen ions

Substance: Benzoic acid. $C_7H_6O_2$ = 122·1. *Temperature:* 20°.
Concentration: 0·01M at half-neutralization. Benzoic acid (0·0611 g.), dried overnight in a vacuum desiccator (H_2SO_4, 20 mm., 20°), was dissolved in 47·5 ml. of water by magnetically stirring for 20 minutes at 40°.

1	2	3	4	5	6	7	8
Titrant 0·1N-KOH ml.	pH	Stoicheiometric concentrations*		$\{H^+\}$†	$\dfrac{[HA]-\{H^+\}}{[A^-]+\{H^+\}}$	log of column 6	pK$_a$ (= pH + column 7)
		[HA]	[A$^-$]				
0·0	3·07	0·010	0				
0·5	3·35	0·009	0·001	0·00045	855/145	+0·77	4·12
1·0	3·59	0·008	0·002	0·00026	774/226	+0·54	4·13
1·5	3·79	0·007	0·003	0·00016	684/316	+0·34	4·13
2·0	3·96	0·006	0·004	0·00011	589/411	+0·16	4·12
2·5	4·14	0·005	0·005	0·00007	493/507	−0·02	4·12
3·0	4·32	0·004	0·006	0·00005	395/605	−0·19	4·13
3·5	4·50	0·003	0·007	0·00003	297/703	−0·37	4·13
4·0	4·71	0·002	0·008	—	200/800	−0·60	4·11
4·5	5·06	0·001	0·009	—	100/900	−0·95	4·11
5·0	6·45	0	0·010	—			

Result: pK$_a$ = 4·12 ($\pm$0·01) at 0·01M and 20°, (using all nine values in the set).

* As defined in Table 2.1.
† From Column 2 and Appendix I (p. 168).

TABLE 2.3

Determination of the ionization constant of a monobasic acid in the form of its sodium salt (cf. the titration of the free acid in Table 2.2)

Substance: Sodium benzoate. $C_7H_5O_2Na = 144.1$. *Temperature:* 20°.
Concentration: 0·01M throughout. Sodium benzoate (0·0721 g.), dried overnight in a vacuum desiccator (H_2SO_4, 20 mm., 20°), was dissolved in 50 ml. of cold water.

1	2	3	4	5	6	7	8
Titrant N-HCl ml.	pH	Stoicheiometric concentrations [HA]	[A⁻]	$\{H^+\}$	$\dfrac{[HA] - \{H^+\}}{[A^-] + \{H^+\}}$	log of column 6	pK_a (= pH + column 7)
0·00	7·07	0	0·010				
0·05	5·06	0·001	0·009	—	100/900	−0·95	4·11
0·10	4·72	0·002	0·008	—	200/800	−0·60	4·12
0·15	4·49	0·003	0·007	0·00003	297/703	−0·37	4·12
0·20	4·30	0·004	0·006	0·00005	395/605	−0·19	4·11
0·25	4·13	0·005	0·005	0·00007	493/507	−0·01	4·12
0·30	3·96	0·006	0·004	0·00011	589/411	+0·15	4·11
0·35	3·78	0·007	0·003	0·00017	683/317	+0·33	4·11
0·40	3·58	0·008	0·002	0·00026	774/226	+0·54	4·12
0·45	3·34	0·009	0·001	0·00046	854/146	+0·77	4·11
0·50	3·07	0·010	0				

Result: $pK_a = 4.12$ (±0·01) at 0·01M and 20° (using all nine values in the set).

TABLE 2.4

Determination of the ionization constant of a monobasic acid requiring correction for the concentration of hydroxyl ions

Substance: p-Cresol. C_7H_8O = 108·13. *Temperature:* 20°.
Concentration: 0·01M at half-neutralization. p-Cresol (0·0541 g.), purified by vacuum distillation, was ground and dried overnight in a vacuum desiccator (H_2SO_4, 20 mm., 20°), and dissolved in 47·5 ml. of ion-free water by magnetically stirring for 30 minutes at 20° under nitrogen.

1	2	3	4	5	6	7	8
Titrant 0·1N-KOH ml.	pH	Stoicheiometric concentrations		$\{OH^-\}$*	$\dfrac{[HA]+\{OH^-\}}{[A^-]-\{OH^-\}}$	log of column 6	pK_a (= pH + column 7)
		[HA]	[A⁻]				
0	6·92	0·010	0	—			
0·5	9·19	0·009	0·001	—	900/100	+0·95	10·14
1·0	9·55	0·008	0·002	0·00002	802/198	+0·61	10·16
1·5	9·77	0·007	0·003	0·00004	704/296	+0·38	10·15
2·0	9·97	0·006	0·004	0·00006	606/394	+0·19	10·16
2·5	10·14	0·005	0·005	0·00010	510/490	+0·02	10·16
3·0	10·29	0·004	0·006	0·00013	413/587	−0·15	10·14
3·5	10·46	0·003	0·007	0·00020	320/680	−0·33	10·13
4·0	10·64	0·002	0·008	0·00030	230/770	−0·53	10·11
4·5	10·84	0·001	0·009	0·00048	148/852	−0·76	10·08
5·0	11·08	0	0·010				

Result: pK_a = 10·14 ($\pm$0·03) at 0·01M and 20° (using the inner seven values of the set).

* From column 2 and Appendix I (p. 168).

TABLE 2.5

Determination of the ionization constant of a monoacidic base requiring no correction for hydrogen or hydroxyl ions

Substance: Amino*tris*hydroxymethylmethane (i.e. the well-known buffer 'Tris'). $H_2N.C(CH_2OH)_3 = C_4H_{11}NO_3 = 121\cdot14$. *Temperature:* 20°.

Concentration: 0·01M throughout. Tris (0·0606 g.), dried for one hour in air at 110°, was dissolved in 50 ml. of ion-free water and titrated under nitrogen (to exclude carbon dioxide).

1	2	3	4	5	6	7
Titrant N-HCl ml.	pH	Stoicheiometric concentrations*		$\dfrac{[BH^+]}{[B]}$	log of column 5	pK_a (= pH + column 6)
		[BH⁺]	[B]			
0	10·12	0	0·010			
0·05	9·12	0·001	0·009	1/9	−0·95	8·17
0·10	8·78	0·002	0·008	2/8	−0·60	8·18
0·15	8·55	0·003	0·007	3/7	−0·37	8·18
0·20	8·36	0·004	0·006	4/6	−0·18	8·18
0·25	8·19	0·005	0·005	5/5	0·00	8·19
0·30	8·01	0·006	0·004	6/4	+0·18	8·19
0·35	7·81	0·007	0·003	7/3	+0·37	8·18
0·40	7·57	0·008	0·002	8/2	+0·60	8·17
0·45	7·21	0·009	0·001	9/1	+0·95	8·16
0·50	4·32	0·010	0			

Result: $pK_a = 8\cdot18$ (±0·02) at 0·01M and 20° (using all nine values in the set).

* As defined in Table 2.1.

TABLE 2.6

Determination of the ionization constant of a monoacidic base requiring correction for the concentration of hydrogen ions

Substance: p-Chloroaniline ($C_6H_6NCl = 127.57$). *Temperature:* 20°.
Concentration: 0·01M throughout. p-Chloroaniline (0·0638 g.), purified by vacuum distillation, ground and dried overnight in a vacuum desiccator ($CaCl_2$, 20 mm., 20°), was dissolved in 50 ml. of water by magnetically stirring at 40° for 30 minutes.

1	2	3	4	5	6	7	8
Titrant N-HCl ml.	pH	Stoicheiometric concentrations		$\{H^+\}$*	$\dfrac{[BH^+]-\{H^+\}}{[B]+\{H^+\}}$	log of column 6	pK$_a$ (= pH + column 7)
		$[BH^+]$	$[B]$				
0	6·72	0	0·010				
0·05	4·85	0·001	0·009	—	100/900	−0·95	3·90
0·10	4·52	0·002	0·008	0·00003	197/803	−0·61	3·91
0·15	4·31	0·003	0·007	0·00005	295/705	−0·38	3·93
0·20	4·14	0·004	0·006	0·00007	393/607	−0·19	3·95
0·25	3·96	0·005	0·005	0·00011	489/511	−0·02	3·94
0·30	3·81	0·006	0·004	0·00015	585/415	+0·15	3·96
0·35	3·64	0·007	0·003	0·00023	677/323	+0·32	3·96
0·40	3·43	0·008	0·002	0·00037	763/237	+0·51	3·94
0·45	3·20	0·009	0·001	0·00063	837/163	+0·71	3·91
0·50	2·95	0·010	0				

Result: pK$_a$ = 3·93 (±0.03) at 0·01M and 20° (using all nine values in the set).

* From column 2, and Appendix I (p. 168).

TABLE 2.7

Determination of the ionization constant of a monoacidic base requiring correction for the concentration of hydroxyl ions

Substance: Glycine. $C_2H_5NO_2 = 75.07$. *Temperature:* 20°.
Concentration: 0·01M at half-neutralization. Glycine (0·0375 g.), recrystallized from water and dried in air at 110° for an hour, was dissolved in 47·5 ml. of ion-free water and titrated under nitrogen (to exclude carbon dioxide).

1	2	3	4	5	6	7	8
Titrant 0·1N-KOH	pH	Stoicheiometric concentrations		$\{OH^-\}$*	$\dfrac{[BH^+]+\{OH^-\}}{[B]-\{OH^-\}}$	log of column 6	pK_a ($= pH +$ column 7)
		$[BH^+]$	$[B]$				
0	6·30	0·010	0	—			
0·5	8·94	0·009	0·001	—	900/100	+0·95	9·89
1·0	9·28	0·008	0·002	—	800/200	+0·60	9·88
1·5	9·50	0·007	0·003	0·00002	702/298	+0·37	9·87
2·0	9·69	0·006	0·004	0·00003	603/397	+0·18	9·87
2·5	9·88	0·005	0·005	0·00005	505/495	+0·01	9·89
3·0	10·05	0·004	0·006	0·00008	408/592	−0·16	9·89
3·5	10·23	0·003	0·007	0·00015	315/685	−0·34	9·89
4·0	10·42	0·002	0·008	0·00018	218/782	−0·55	9·87
4·5	10·68	0·001	0·009	0·00033	133/867	−0·81	9·87
5·0	11·01	0	0·010				

Result: $pK_a = 9.88$ (± 0.01) at 0·01M and 20° (using all nine values in the set).

* From column 2, and Appendix I (p. 168).

Common sources of error, and their elimination

One of the commonest errors in titrating with alkali is for the values, in the set of pK_a values, to show an *upward trend* as the titration progresses. This is usually caused by an impurity in the substance undergoing determination, so that not so much of it is present as had been supposed. By far the commonest and most troublesome impurity is water. To avoid this trouble, every substance submitted for determination of pK_a should be of analytical purity and dried under the same conditions that preceded its analysis. Another possible cause of an upward pH trend is that the stream of nitrogen is too fast and is expelling some of the solution as a spray. Another cause of an upward trend is that the correct amount of material is present throughout the titration but not all of it is in solution. In the presence of undissolved material, no satisfactory pK_a value can be reached.

When titrating with acid, a *downward trend* can be due to the same causes as given in the last paragraph for an upward trend with alkali.

Another common source of error is that the titrant is not added in exactly the desired volume. Sometimes this is due to inexperience in manipulation, but sometimes the burette is in error.

Sometimes the required degree of precision is not obtained because the method is not suitable for the substance (pp. 10–12 may be re-read in this connexion).

An incongruous set of results often indicates that decomposition is occurring during titration. Sometimes the first few readings give concordant pKs, after which decomposition causes a drift of potential. Those substances which are easily decomposed by acid or alkali are often attacked by each drop of titrant, even in well stirred solutions. Sometimes back-titration gives a different set of pH values from the forward titration, whereupon a second forward titration retraces the pH values of the first (i.e. a hysteresis loop is formed). This indicates a slow and quantitative interconversion of two related substances, which may be tautomers, or they may have a ring-chain relationship, or one may be a covalent hydrate of the other. Pseudo-acids (e.g. nitromethane) and pseudo-bases (e.g. triphenylmethane dyes and quaternary N-heterocycles) also show this phenomenon and equilibration may take anything from an hour to a week. For suitable methods for tackling covalent hydration* and pseudo-base formation,† the literature should be consulted: normal mass action relationships are followed, and equilibrium constants can be extracted from the data, quite apart from any study of the kinetics of the reaction.

Ill-defined acidic or basic constants are often obtained at low pH values, especially below pH 2. In some cases the substance really has acidic or basic properties, as suggested by the pK_a, but the result has too great a spread to be acceptable. These results arise when the pK_a is equal to, or slightly above, the logarithm of the dilution. In one base which we investigated (the concentration was 0·05M and hence the dilution was 20, and the log dilution 1·3), the pK_a seemed to be $1·45 \pm 0·13$ (volume corrections for the added titrant had been made as on p. 29). Such a large spread is inadmissible, and the error was traced to the use of activities and concentrations in the same equation, i.e. $\{H^+\}$ had been calculated as antilog $(0 - pH)$, and this *activity* term had been combined with stoicheiometric *concentration* terms for [B] and [BH$^+$]. When the concentration term [BH$^+$] was converted to an activity term, as on pp. 62–64, a satisfactory thermodynamic pK_a of $1·25 \pm 0·05$ was obtained (see p. 57). The use of $\{H^+\}$ with concentration terms does not give trouble if the pK_a is 1·5 units, or more, above the logarithm of the dilution.

False constants

When a pK_a appears, in a titration, to be well below the logarithm of the dilution at which it was found, it is almost certainly a mirage (false constant) and the substance being titrated has no acidic or basic properties in that region. Thus the titration of plain water (4·75 ml.), with 0·5 ml. of N-HCl, gives a pK_a of $0·62 \pm 0·07$

---

* ALBERT, BROWN and CHEESEMAN, *J. Chem. Soc.*, 1952, 1620; PERRIN and INOUE, *Proc. Chem. Soc.*, 1960, 342.
† GOLDACRE and PHILLIPS, *J. Chem. Soc.*, 1949, 1724.

(even if correction is made for dilution by the titrant), so long as no activity correction is performed. This result is clearly absurd. Yet, had an inert substance been dissolved in the water (say at $0.1M$), it may have been credited with this pK_a, although the fact that the logarithm of the dilution is 1.0 should put the investigator on his guard.

False acidic or basic constants can also be found in glass-electrode titrations where most of the pH readings are higher than 11. For example, 100 ml. of boiled-out water, titrated with 5.0 ml. of $0.1N$-potassium hydroxide, gave a false pK_a of 12.11 ± 0.05 (calculations based as on a $0.005M$ solution). Had $0.005M$ of an inert substance been present, it might have been credited with this constant. Very high and very low pK_a values in the literature should be scrutinized carefully before being accepted.

3

Refinements of
Potentiometric Titration:
Apparatus and Calculations

A. APPARATUS

Semi-micro-titrations

The method described in Chapter 2 can be scaled down, with no loss of accuracy and with a small gain in speed. It can be used for as little as one twenty-thousandth of a mole dissolved in 10 ml. of water (0·005M). This effects a great economy of material. A balance weighing accurately to 10 micrograms (i.e. a good 'five-place' balance) is required, also a micrometer syringe to deliver 0·5 ml. of 0·1N titrant in 0·050-ml. portions. The minimal volume of solution that can be titrated is 10 ml. (in a 30-ml. beaker): no smaller volume will cover the standard electrode assembly shown in Fig. 2.1. We have found this method very useful for routine determinations on new substances and have used it regularly since 1954. For more concentrated solutions, or for smaller fractions of a mole, a micro-titration should be performed.

Micro-titrations

Although commercial apparatus is available for micro-titrations, much of this is fragile or hard to clean. The apparatus shown in Fig. 3.1 can be put together from easily accessible materials plus a miniature glass electrode. With its aid as little as 0·5 mg. of a substance, dissolved in 0·5 ml. of water, can readily be titrated. In this way, ionization constants can be used to help identify small fractions isolated in chromatography, and the

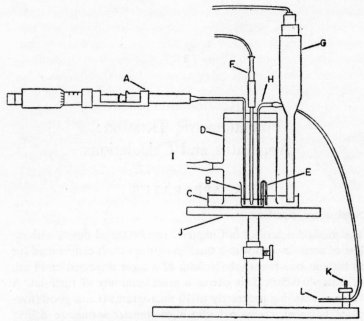

Fig. 3.1. Apparatus for micro-determination of ionization constants by potentiometry

A, Micrometer syringe. B, Titration vessel. C, Petri dish containing saturated KCl solution. D, Glass shield and stopper (supported as described on p. 45). E, Salt bridge. F, Miniature glass electrode. G, Calomel electrode (full size). H, Nitrogen delivery tube for stirring. I, Nitrogen delivery tube for supplying an inert atmosphere. J, Adjustable platform. K, Precision pinchcock. L, Entry for moist, oxygen-free nitrogen from aspirator shown in Fig. 3.3

solution remaining after titration can be used for ultraviolet spectroscopy.

The apparatus of Fig. 3.1 is suitable for volumes of solution from 0·5 to 5·0 ml. It should be located in a thermostatically controlled room. A petri dish, 9 cm. in diameter and containing saturated potassium chloride solution, is placed centrally on the adjustable platform. The titration vessel is a flat-bottomed tube of glass or polythene. It should be 20–30 mm. high and have a diameter in the range 10–20 mm. according to the volume required. Electrical contact between the solution to be titrated and the potassium chloride solution in the dish is made by a salt bridge constructed as in Fig. 3.2. Thus, glass tubing of 7 mm. diameter is drawn out to about 1 mm. diameter. A U-shaped bend is made by carefully warming this capillary tube over a pilot flame so that one limb is about 30 mm. longer than the other. The distance between the limbs should be 2 to 3 mm. A right-angled bend is made where the thin and thick portions of the tubing meet. The longer limb is placed in a warm solution of agar (0·3 g.) dissolved in saturated aqueous potassium chloride (10 ml.) and a slight suction is applied so that the solution fills the capillary completely. When the agar is cool and set, the limbs are cut to an equal length. The bridge is suspended on the rim of the titration vessel. Such bridges are stored in saturated potassium chloride solution when not in use. The level of the solution in the petri dish should be adjusted so that it is about 2 mm. above the level of the solution in the titration vessel.

The miniature glass electrode is supported above the adjustable platform in a glass shield by a rubber bung from which a 10° sector has been removed to admit the micrometer syringe needle used in titration. A 3-mm. (diameter) hole is drilled in the bung to take a glass capillary used to distribute nitrogen for stirring. Both the needle and the capillary dip into the solution to be titrated. The glass shield is a cylinder, about 35 mm. in diameter and 55 mm. in height. It is fitted with a side arm through which nitrogen can be passed if an inert atmosphere is required because the amount of nitrogen used in stirring is not enough for this purpose. The glass electrode is positioned so that the tip is 1 mm. above the lower edge of the shield and about 50 mm. above the top of the petri dish when the platform is in the fully lowered position. The shield and the electrode are rigidly held by clips (e.g. Terry clips) which are screwed into the ends of pieces of wooden dowelling which can be held, by bossheads, to a small retort stand (not shown in Fig. 3.1). If the apparatus is used frequently, a further refinement is to supply rack-and-pinion movements to control the height of the platform and to locate and lower the micrometer syringe.

The (saturated) calomel electrode is attached in a similar way to the same vertical support. It is positioned outside the glass shield so that its sintered plug is at the same level as the lower edge of the glass shield.

The substance whose ionization constant is to be determined is weighed directly into the tared titration vessel. Water is added and the substance is dissolved (by careful warming if necessary). After cooling, the volume of the solution is determined by weighing the vessel and its contents to the nearest milligram.

The miniature glass electrode is checked for linearity with phthalate and borate buffers as described on p. 19. The electrode is then rapidly washed. This washing is conveniently done with an ungraduated pipette of about 15 ml. capacity fitted with a rubber bulb. A 45° bend about 15 mm. from the end of the capillary enables a jet of water to be directed upwards towards the glass electrode. The adhering droplets can be removed from the electrode and shield with small pieces of filter paper. The titration should be begun immediately after standardization and washing are complete. To this end, the salt bridge is placed in position and the vessel is raised (by raising the petri dish) so that the bulb of the glass electrode dips into the solution.

Purified nitrogen gas from a reservoir of about 500 ml. capacity (Fig. 3.3) is passed through a narrow-bore polythene tube to the stirring capillary. The rate of flow is controlled at about 2 bubbles per second by a precision pinchcock (e.g. the Pregl type, obtainable from Gallenkamp & Co., London, catalogue no. b-13598). The flow of nitrogen is maintained whilst each portion of the titrant is being added and for about one minute longer. The flow is stopped, by closing the stopcock on the reservoir, before reading the pH. Equilibrium is reached in about one minute after the nitrogen ceases to flow.

If a thermostatically controlled room is not available, the petri dish should be jacketed (i.e. made double-walled). Water from a thermostatically controlled bath can be circulated through the

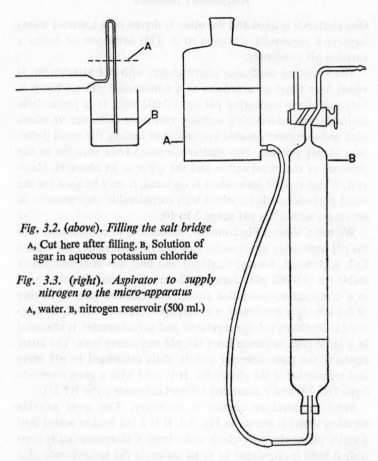

Fig. 3.2. (above). Filling the salt bridge
A, Cut here after filling. B, Solution of
agar in aqueous potassium chloride

*Fig. 3.3. (right). Aspirator to supply
nitrogen to the micro-apparatus*
A, water. B, nitrogen reservoir (500 ml.)

jacket to maintain the temperature in the titration vessel as
required ±0·5°.

The vibrating condenser electrometer
This type of instrument, known also as the vibrating-reed amplifier,
was developed in recent years to measure very small currents with
great accuracy. The working part, outwardly resembling a radio
valve, has two electrode surfaces separated by a small air gap.

47

One electrode is fixed and the other is driven by a solenoid which imparts a sinusoidal vibration to it. This arrangement forms a variable air condenser.

The vibrating condenser electrometer, with pH attachment, is about four times as expensive as a commercial pH set but it is very useful for measuring pH to $\pm0\cdot002$ unit. It is particularly desirable for determining stability constants (Chapter 9) where each measurement consists essentially of finding the small difference in pH between two similar titrations (one titration in the presence of the metal cation and the other in its absence). However, if this type of instrument is on hand, it may be used for the usual potentiometric titrations with considerable improvement in accuracy, within the pH range 3 to 10.

We use a Vibron Electrometer, model 33B in conjunction with the pH measuring attachment, type C 33B (Electronic Instruments Ltd, Richmond, Surrey, England) and find that it is completely stable (to $\pm0\cdot002$ pH) during 24 hours, provided that it is used in a temperature-controlled room. The electrometer, consisting of the vibrating condenser, a.c. amplifier, rectifier circuit, stabilizing d.c. feedback voltage regulator, and galvanometer, is mounted in a large case, separate from the pH measuring unit. The latter contains the potentiometer circuit, dials calibrated in pH units and terminals for the electrodes. It is used with a glass electrode (type GG 33) and a saturated calomel electrode (type RJ 23).

Strict temperature control is necessary. The most suitable titration vessel is shown in Fig. 3.4. It is a tall beaker sealed into a water jacket through which water from a thermostatically controlled bath is circulated so as to maintain the temperature of a solution in the beaker at the required temperature $\pm0\cdot02°$. The electrode assembly is as in Fig. 2.1 except that magnetic stirring is preferred to stirring by nitrogen bubbles. Stirring is continued for one minute after each addition, and discontinued while readings are being taken. If an atmosphere of nitrogen is required, moist, oxygen-freed gas should be directed across the surface of the liquid.

Low resistance glass electrodes

Electrodes of large diameter (3 cm.) and low resistance (0·5 MΩ) are supplied by the Janaer Glaswerk, Bavaria. These require no amplifier and give results as precise as those obtainable with a hydrogen electrode, viz. ±0·002 pH unit, or 0·1 mv. This high precision* arises from the possibility that these electrodes afford for compensating for variations in asymmetry potential; however, they have proved rather troublesome in use.

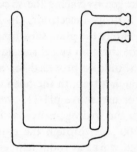

Fig. 3.4. Glass titration vessel with sealed-on water jacket

The hydrogen electrode

This consists of a platinum or gold wire (or plate) on which a very thin, catalytically active layer of finely divided platinum is deposited. These electrodes may be readily bought, or else made according to Hildebrand.† They require some care in maintenance.‡ Some highly accurate determinations of pK_a have been made with the hydrogen electrode used in cells without liquid junctions.§

In general, the hydrogen electrode is cumbersome, and less useful than the glass electrode because it is easily poisoned by

* COVINGTON and PRUE, *J. Chem. Soc.*, 1955, 3696; KING and PRUE, ibid., 1961, 275.
† HILDEBRAND, *J. Amer. Chem. Soc.*, 1913, **35**, p. 847.
‡ KOLTHOFF and LAITINEN, *pH and Electro-titrations*. New York: Wiley, 1931.
§ HARNED and EHLERS, *J. Amer. Chem. Soc.*, 1932, **54**, 1350; HARNED and OWEN, *The Physical Chemistry of Electrolytic Solutions*. New York: Reinhold, 1950, p. 497.

compounds of sulphur, mercury or arsenic. Also it may hydrogenate the substance being investigated. It is most used for potentiometric titration of substances having a pK_a in excess of 11, i.e. in a region where the glass electrode is likely to be inaccurate. However, it is useless in the presence of oxidizing or reducing substances for which it would record the oxidation–reduction potential.

The apparatus is set up as in Fig. 2.1 (p. 21), but with the hydrogen electrode replacing the glass electrode, and a stream of hydrogen (replacing the stream of nitrogen) directed at the tip of the hydrogen electrode. (In another type of electrode the hydrogen enters the glass sheathing of the platinum wire.) The stopper of the titration vessel should be tight-fitting, and an extra opening should be provided for a tube that will convey the excess gas, through a trap, to the open air outside the building.

For use above pH 11, every trace of oxygen must be removed from the hydrogen, by passing it either over platinized asbestos at 500°, or through the commercial chromous salt apparatus,* which works at room temperature.

The titration vessel should be placed in a thermostat, and the cell checked against potassium hydrogen phthalate buffer. Although nothing so elaborate as a commercial pH set is required to obtain readings from this electrode assembly, such a set is always present in the laboratory and most models can conveniently be used as a millivolt potentiometer for the purpose.

For an example of the use of the hydrogen electrode in the pK_a 12–14 range see Thamsen.† Because of the high sensitivity of the hydrogen electrode to temperature variations, it is imperative to standardize the electrodes at the same temperature at which the titration is conducted.

Micro-titrations with the hydrogen electrodes can be made in a small, horizontally elongated cell of capacity 0·15 ml.,‡ with three tubulatures. Hydrogen enters by one tubulature, flows over

* e.g. 'Nilox', Southern Analytical Ltd, Camberley, Surrey, England.
† THAMSEN, *Acta Chem. Scand.*, 1952, **6**, 270.
‡ OGSTON and PETERS, *Biochem. J.*, 1936, **30**, 736.

the surface of the solution, passes the centrally situated electrode and escapes through the last tubulature to the open air, via a trap. Contact of the electrode with hydrogen, as well as adequate mixing, is assured by keeping the cell mechanically rocked through an angle of 20° about three times a second. The calomel reference electrode is connected through a capillary and stopcock attached to the bottom of the cell. The apparatus is maintained in an air thermostat at the required temperature ± 0.2.

The rapid-flow method

When a substance is stable in one ionic species, but unstable in another, a rapid mixing of the solution with a stoicheiometric amount of the titrant is not difficult to arrange shortly before the mixture streams past the electrodes. Such an arrangement has been described for amidines* which are stable as cations, but unstable as neutral molecules. Because of the high pH values involved, this example uses the hydrogen electrode; but at lower pH values, the glass electrode can be used instead.

B. CALCULATIONS

Polyelectrolytes

Many substances have two ionizing groups. If these are both acidic groups, they can be titrated sequentially with two equivalents of alkali; if both groups are basic they can similarly be titrated with two equivalents of acid. No special calculations are required for most titrations of this kind (the precision of results involving a di-cation or di-anion can be sharpened by applying special activity corrections, as on p. 64).

However, when it is indicated by the titration that two ionizing groups are separated by less than 2·7 units of pK_a, the usual calculations can only give results of poor precision. The end-point of the first equivalent is unsharp because the titration of one group begins before that of the other is completed. An accurate result

---

* SCHWARZENBACH, *Helv. chim. Acta*, 1940, 23, 1162.

can be obtained with the application of the following method of calculation, which is due to Noyes.*

Let C be the total concentration (all species) of the acid being titrated. Let B be the concentration of the alkali added. (In a back-titration, B = 2C less the concentration of acid added from the burette.)

$$\text{Let } X = \{H^+\}(B - C + \{H^+\})$$
$$Y = 2C - (B + \{H^+\})$$
$$Z = \{H^+\}^2(B + \{H^+\})$$

No term [OH⁻] is used, even for readings above pH 10.

Let X_1, Y_1, Z_1, refer to readings obtained with less than one equivalent of titrant, and let X_2, Y_2, Z_2 refer to readings obtained with more than one equivalent of titrant.

Then,

$$K_{a1} = \frac{Y_1 Z_2 - Y_2 Z_1}{X_1 Y_2 - X_2 Y_1} \quad \text{and} \quad K_{a2} = \frac{X_1 Z_2 - X_2 Z_1}{Y_1 Z_2 - Y_2 Z_1} \quad (3.1)$$

Pairs of readings are selected from either side of the mid-point; the selection is preferably, but not necessarily, symmetrical.

This involves a good deal of calculation, but is entirely straightforward; without it, accurate values cannot be derived from the titration.

For a base, the same calculations apply, except that the formula K_{a1} (above) gives K_{a2}, and vice versa.

Phosphoric acid, with pK_a values 2·2, 7·1 and 12·3, is an example of a polyelectrolyte not needing a Noyes correction, whereas citric acid, with pK_a values 3·1, 4·7 and 6·4, obviously needs such correction.

Table 3·1 affords an example of a substance (succinic acid) which has pK_a values close enough to influence one another. The uncorrected values in column 3 were worked out as for a pair of monocarboxylic acids, as in Table 2.1. It is seen, by reference to the true values in column 4 (obtained by the Noyes method as shown in Table 3.2) that little indication of the true pK_a is to be

* NOYES, *Z. physik. Chem.*, 1893, **11**, 495; cf. BRITTON, *Hydrogen Ions*. London: Chapman & Hall, 1955.

obtained in this way. It is significant that half the sum of the two pK$_a$ values is almost exactly 4·78, which is the pH of half-neutralization (this relationship between the pK$_a$ values of a polyelectrolyte is not observed in practice if they are more widely separated than 2·5 units of pK).

TABLE 3.1

Determinations of ionization constants of a dibasic acid, requiring separation of overlapping pK$_a$ values

Substance: Succinic acid, $C_4H_6O_4 = 118·09$. *Temperature:* 20°.
Concentration: 0·01M at three-quarter neutralization; corrected for increasing volume as on p. 29. Succinic acid (0·0590 g.), twice recrystallized from warm water and dried overnight (H_2SO_4, 20 mm., 20°), was dissolved in 42·5 ml. of ion-free water.

1	2	3	4
Titrant 0·1N-KOH	pH	Unseparated pK$_a$ values (obtained as in Table 2.1)	Separated pK$_a$ values (obtained as in Table 3.2)
0·0	3·02		
0·5	3·28	4·03	—
1·0	3·52	4·05	4·07
1·5	3·71	4·04	4·07
2·0	3·89	4·04	4·07
2·5	4·05	4·03	4·08
3·0	4·20	4·01	4·09
3·5	4·35	3·97	4·12
4·0	4·48	3·87	4·11
4·5	4·64	3·66	4·12
5·0	4·78	—	—
5·5	4·92	5·87	5·42
6·0	5·05	5·65	5·42
6·5	5·20	5·57	5·43
7·0	5·34	5·52	5·44
7·5	5·48	5·48	5·43
8·0	5·63	5·45	5·43
8·5	5·79	5·42	5·39
9·0	6·02	5·42	5·40
9·5	6·35	5·40	—
10·0	8·12		

Results: pK$_{a1}$ = 4·09 ± 0·03
pK$_{a2}$ = 5·42 ± 0·03, at 0·01M and 20°.

TABLE 3.2

Succinic acid 0·01M

Separation of overlapping values. See p. 52 for definition of symbols.

See p. 52 for definition of symbols.

0·1N-KOH ml.	C	B	{H+}	X	Y	Z	Y_1Z_2	Y_1Z_1
4·5	0·0106	0·0096	$2·29 \times 10^{-5}$	$-2·244 \times 10^{-8}$	0·0116	$5·045 \times 10^{-12}$	$1·922 \times 10^{-14}$	$4·692 \times 10^{-14}$
5·5	0·0104	0·0115	$1·20 \times 10^{-5}$	$1·334 \times 10^{-8}$	0·0093	$1·657 \times 10^{-12}$		
4·0	0·0108	0·0086	$3·31 \times 10^{-6}$	$-7·183 \times 10^{-8}$	0·0130	$9·455 \times 10^{-12}$	$1·28 \times 10^{-14}$	$7·753 \times 10^{-14}$
6·0	0·0103	0·0124	$8·91 \times 10^{-6}$	$1·879 \times 10^{-8}$	0·0082	$9·844 \times 10^{-13}$		
3·5	0·0109	0·0076	$4·47 \times 10^{-5}$	$-1·457 \times 10^{-7}$	0·0142	$1·526 \times 10^{-11}$	$7·520 \times 10^{-15}$	$1·083 \times 10^{-13}$
6·5	0·0102	0·0133	$6·31 \times 10^{-6}$	$1·960 \times 10^{-8}$	0·0071	$5·296 \times 10^{-13}$		
3·0	0·0110	0·0066	$6·31 \times 10^{-5}$	$-2·739 \times 10^{-7}$	0·0153	$2·652 \times 10^{-11}$	$4·506 \times 10^{-15}$	$1·618 \times 10^{-13}$
7·0	0·0101	0·0141	$4·57 \times 10^{-6}$	$1·830 \times 10^{-8}$	0·0061	$2·945 \times 10^{-13}$		
2·5	0·0111	0·0056	$8·91 \times 10^{-5}$	$-4·820 \times 10^{-7}$	0·0165	$4·517 \times 10^{-11}$	$2·711 \times 10^{-15}$	$2·259 \times 10^{-13}$
7·5	0·0100	0·0150	$3·31 \times 10^{-6}$	$1·656 \times 10^{-8}$	0·0050	$1·643 \times 10^{-13}$		
2·0	0·0112	0·0045	$1·29 \times 10^{-4}$	$-8·475 \times 10^{-7}$	0·0178	$7·705 \times 10^{-11}$	$1·540 \times 10^{-15}$	$3·082 \times 10^{-13}$
8·0	0·0099	0·0158	$2·34 \times 10^{-6}$	$1·38 \times 10^{-8}$	0·0040	$8·651 \times 10^{-14}$		
1·5	0·0114	0·0034	$1·95 \times 10^{-4}$	$-1·521 \times 10^{-6}$	0·0192	$1·369 \times 10^{-10}$	$8·415 \times 10^{-16}$	$3·970 \times 10^{-13}$
8·5	0·0098	0·0167	$1·62 \times 10^{-6}$	$1·118 \times 10^{-8}$	0·0029	$4·383 \times 10^{-14}$		
1·0	0·0115	0·0023	$3·02 \times 10^{-4}$	$-2·688 \times 10^{-6}$	0·0204	$2·371 \times 10^{-10}$	$3·256 \times 10^{-16}$	$4·505 \times 10^{-13}$
9·0	0·0097	0·0175	$9·55 \times 10^{-7}$	$7·449 \times 10^{-9}$	0·0019	$1·596 \times 10^{-14}$		

(continuation of Table 3.2)

0.1N-KOH ml.	X_1Y_2	X_2Y_1	X_1Z_2	X_2Z_1	$Y_1Z_2 - Y_2Z_1$	$X_1Y_2 - X_2Y_1$	$X_1Z_2 - X_2Z_1$	pK_1	pK_2
4.5 5.5	-2.087×10^{-10}	1.547×10^{-10}	-3.718×10^{-20}	6.730×10^{-20}	-2.770×10^{-14}	-3.634×10^{-10}	-1.045×10^{-19}	4.12	5.42
4.0 6.0	-5.890×10^{-10}	2.443×10^{-10}	-7.071×10^{-20}	1.777×10^{-19}	-6.473×10^{-14}	-8.333×10^{-10}	-2.484×10^{-19}	4.11	5.42
3.5 6.5	-1.034×10^{-9}	2.783×10^{-10}	-7.716×10^{-20}	2.991×10^{-19}	-1.008×10^{-13}	-1.312×10^{-9}	-3.763×10^{-19}	4.12	5.43
3.0 7.0	-1.671×10^{-9}	2.800×10^{-10}	-8.066×10^{-20}	4.853×10^{-19}	-1.573×10^{-13}	-1.951×10^{-9}	-5.660×10^{-19}	4.09	5.44
2.5 7.5	-2.410×10^{-9}	2.732×10^{-10}	-7.919×10^{-20}	7.480×10^{-19}	-2.232×10^{-13}	-2.683×10^{-9}	-8.272×10^{-19}	4.08	5.43
2.0 8.0	-3.390×10^{-9}	2.458×10^{-10}	-7.332×10^{-20}	1.064×10^{-18}	-3.067×10^{-13}	-3.636×10^{-9}	-1.137×10^{-18}	4.07	5.43
1.5 8.5	-4.411×10^{-9}	2.147×10^{-10}	-6.667×10^{-20}	1.531×10^{-18}	-3.962×10^{-13}	-4.626×10^{-9}	-1.598×10^{-18}	4.07	5.39
1.0 9.0	-5.107×10^{-9}	1.520×10^{-10}	-4.290×10^{-20}	1.766×10^{-18}	-4.502×10^{-13}	-5.259×10^{-9}	-1.809×10^{-18}	4.07	5.40

When one acidic and one basic group are present in the same substance, these may be titrated separately with alkali and acid respectively. Overlapping values are not so often encountered, but may be treated as in Table 3.2. The more difficult problem of deciding whether or not the substance is a zwitterion is discussed in Chapter 7.

Molecules with a large number of ionizing groups present special difficulties even when all the groups are structurally identical as in polyacrylic acid. The high molecular weight of such substances endows them with special properties and places them, along with polypeptides and nucleotides, in a class of substances which is becoming more and more the province of the bio-physicist.

The titration curves of polyelectrolytes have an indefinite ('smeared-out') appearance. In titrating a polyelectrolyte, the curve should be plotted. The inflexions can then be located by seeking the position of maximal increment in pH following equal additions of alkali. A uniform ionic strength should be maintained for the following reason. A polyion dissolved in plain water tends to expand until like charges are as far from one another as possible. But during the titration, the ionic strength increases as titrant is added. In proportion to this increase, contraction of the molecule usually occurs, so that pK values are constantly shifting. A swamping concentration of potassium chloride, if present throughout the titration, keeps the substance in its contracted form. Contrary to what happens with mono- and di-ions, a large fraction of the counterions ('gegenions') of a polyion remain physically close to it.

Even with the precaution of ensuring constant ionic strength, it is not possible to obtain a precise pK_a for any group in a *highly* polybasic acid. This follows from Kern's equation:*
$pK_a = pK_o + BpH$ where pK_o is the pK of one representative ionizing group in the polyelectrolyte, and B is a constant. Thus pK_a is constant only for a given pH, and the higher the pH, the weaker each acid group seems to become.

* KERN, *Z. physik. Chem.*, 1938, A **181**, 269.

Activity coefficients

Thus far, we have been able to recommend methods for obtaining satisfactory accuracy without invoking activity corrections. However, it must be emphasized that the ionization constants obtained by these methods are 'mixed constants', e.g. for acids, they lie between the concentration ionization constants and the thermodynamic ionization constants which have become so familiar through conductivity work (see p. 102). These mixed constants, which we call K_a^M, are constant only for the concentration of ionized species at which the pH was measured. The equations of Chapter 2 stand in contrast to equation (3.2), in which all terms are expressed as activities, and which yields the thermodynamic ionization constant (K_a^T), which is independent of concentration; and to the equation (3.3), which is entirely in terms of concentration, and which gives the concentration ionization constant (K_a^C) which varies with the concentration.

$$K_a^T = \frac{\{H^+\}\{A^-\}}{\{HA\}} \qquad (3.2)$$

$$K_a^C = \frac{[H^+][A^-]}{[HA]} \text{ (for an acid), and } \frac{[H^+][B]}{[BH^+]} \text{ (for a base)} \qquad (3.3)$$

We shall now show how our calculations, up to this point, have included both concentration and activity terms, and we shall go on to discuss special conditions where this mixing of terms requires the application of corrections.

We know that [HA], not being an ion, has an activity practically equal to its concentration, and that the hydrogen ion term, as measured potentiometrically, is for all practical purposes the hydrogen ion activity $\{H^+\}$ and quite different from the hydrogen ion concentration $[H^+]$ (see Appendix I, and British Standard Specification No. 1647 (1961)). Thus the principal terms in need of activity correction are $[A^-]$ for acids and $[BH^+]$ for bases. The implication of the activity concept is that not all of an ion is completely free; this is because of electrostatic attraction between oppositely charged ions in solution. The activity of an ion is related to its concentration by the expression:

$$\{A^-\} = [A^-] \times f_i \qquad (3.4)$$

where f_i, known as the activity coefficient of the ion, is usually less than one. This coefficient should increase with increasing dilution until, at infinite dilution, f_i is equal to one, whereupon $K_a^T = K_a^C$.

The constant obtained in potentiometric titration (K_a^M) differs* from K_a^C and K_a^T, in that it has one activity term $\{H^+\}$ and one concentration term $[A^-]$ (it is a matter of indifference whether the concentration of non-ionized acid is written $[HA]$ or $\{HA\}$).

In some circumstances (listed on p. 60) it is desirable to convert K_a^M to K_a^T. A few words on activity theory will now follow so that the nature of the correction process can be understood.

The general formulation of the relationship between the concentration of an ion and its activity coefficient is based on the work of Debye and Hückel.† An important term in this formulation is the 'ionic strength', written as I (or μ) and defined thus:

$$I = 0.5 \Sigma C_i z^2 \qquad (3.5)$$

where C_i is the molar concentration of an ion and z is its valency, and the symbol (Σ) denotes summation. For the common case of a uni-univalent electrolyte, e.g. sodium benzoate, this expression becomes reduced to $I = C_{total}$.

According to Debye and Hückel, the activity coefficient (f_i) of an ion of valence z is given by:

$$-\log f_i = \frac{Az^2\sqrt{I}}{1 + B\,a_i\sqrt{I}} \qquad (3.6)$$

Where A and B are constants which vary with the dielectric constant and temperature of the solvent. For dilute aqueous solutions $A = 0.505$ and $B = 0.328 \times 10^8$ at $20°$. The term a_i is the ionic size parameter, i.e. the mean distance of approach of the ions, for which 5×10^{-8} may be taken as an average value. To convert equation (3.6) to a form where it gives information about *two*

---

* For acids the K_a^M values are intermediate between K_a^C and K_a^T; for bases the pK_a^M values are higher than $K_a^C = K_a^T$. K_a^M is the 'apparent ionization constant (K′)' of certain authors, a term which we cannot recommend.

† DEBYE and HÜCKEL, *Physikal. Z.*, 1923, **24**, 185, 305; 1924, **25**, 145.

kinds of ion, oppositely charged and simultaneously present, we can write:

$$-\log f_{\pm} = \frac{A\, z^{+}z^{-}\sqrt{I}}{1 + B\, a_i\sqrt{I}} = \frac{0{\cdot}505\, z^{+}z^{-}\sqrt{I}}{1 + 1{\cdot}6\sqrt{I}} \text{ at } 20° \quad (3.7)$$

where $f_{\pm}$ is the *mean ionic activity coefficient*, and z^{+} and z^{-} are the valencies of the cation and anion respectively (both must be expressed as *positive* numbers). The desirability of using the *mean* coefficient arises from the fact that it can be confirmed experimentally, whereas the coefficient of a single ion cannot. For the very common case of a uni-univalent (or 1 : 1) electrolyte, the product of z^{+} and z^{-} is 1, which further simplifies equation (3.7), which is satisfactory up to about $I = 0{\cdot}1$ (i.e. $0{\cdot}1$M solution that is fully ionized).

[In solutions more dilute than $0{\cdot}01$M, a univalent ion may be considered as a point charge (i.e. $a = 0$), so that:

$$-\log f_{\pm}^{1:1} = 0{\cdot}505\sqrt{I} \quad (3.8)$$

which is known as the Debye–Hückel limiting law.]

Because pH values, as measured, are defined within the range pH 2 to pH 12, as:

$$\text{pH} = -\log\left(f_{\pm}^{1:1}.[H^{+}]\right) \pm 0{\cdot}02^{*} \quad (3.9)$$

the thermodynamic constant is given by the expression:

$$K_a^T = \frac{\{H^{+}\}[A^{-}]}{[HA]}.f_{\pm}^{1:1} \quad (3.10, a)$$

Hence

$$pK_a^T = \text{pH} + \log\frac{[HA]}{[A^{-}]} \pm \frac{0{\cdot}505\sqrt{I}}{1 + 1{\cdot}6\sqrt{I}} \quad (3.10, b)$$

The last term is positive for acids and negative for bases.

It follows from equations (3.10) that the ionization constants of mixed type (K_a^M) derived in Chapter 2 can be converted to thermodynamic ionization constants as follows:

$$pK_a^T = pK_a^M \pm \frac{0{\cdot}505\sqrt{I}}{1 + 1{\cdot}6\sqrt{I}} \quad (3.11)$$

* British Standard No. 1647, loc. cit.; GOLD, *pH Measurements*. London: Methuen, 1956, p. 38.

Thus a trend would be expected in the values of pK_a^M (as given in the Tables of Chapter 2) as the ionic strength of the solution increases with increasing neutralization. For example, a monobasic acid, titrated at a concentration of 0·01M, requires a correction added to pK_a^M of 0·015 when $[A^-]$ is 0·001, and 0·041 when $[A^-]$ is 0·009 (e.g. benzoic acid in Table 2·2). However, this trend of 0·026 is negligible if, as in routine pK determinations, the measurements are performed with a pH set calibrated in 0·02 pH unit. For this reason we were able to state, in Chapter 2, that titrations may be carried out without activity corrections provided that the concentration does not exceed 0·01M. However, if it is decided to perform a thermodynamic correction on these values, a close approximation can be obtained with the help of equation (3.12), which is a suitable form of (3.11), for these low concentrations, as follows:

$$pK_a^T = pK_a^M + 0.5\sqrt{I_m} \text{ (for acids), or } - 0.5\sqrt{I_m} \text{ (for bases)}$$
$$(3.12)$$

where I_m is the ionic strength at the mid-point of the titration (i.e. for a 0·01M titration, I_m is 0·005). In back-titrations, the ionic strength can be taken as remaining at the concentration of the salt of the unknown acid or base $(I = M)$.

The question must now be asked: when is it advisable to use activity corrections in calculating the results from a potentiometric titration? We recommend that these corrections be applied,

A. if the pH is measured with an instrument calibrated in 0·01 pH units (or greater), and
   (*a*) the concentration lies between 0·01M and 0·1M,* or
   (*b*) the hydrogen ion or hydroxyl ion concentration is comparable in magnitude to the stoicheiometric concentration of the ionized species† (see p. 62, also below), or
   (*c*) the weaker acidic group of a dibasic acid, or the weaker

* 0·1M is considered to be the greatest concentration for which any known activity correction is valid.
† Even with activity correction, the potentiometric method is suitable only for pK_a values in the range 1·3 to 11·0 (glass electrode).

basic group of a diacidic base is titrated at a concentration greater than 0·0025M (see below), or

(d) an extraneous salt is added to achieve 'constant ionic strength'. Also,

B. if the pH is measured with an instrument calibrated in 0·005 pH units or less.

The results in column 3 of Table 3.3 were obtained with the pH attachment of a Vibron Electrometer calibrated in 0·002 pH units. They show a decline in the pK_a^M value of β-naphthol from 9·583 to 9·511 with a rise in ionic strength from 0·011 to 0·096. The pK_a^T in column 4 was obtained by extrapolation of the straight line produced by plotting $\dfrac{\sqrt{I}}{1 + \sqrt{I}}$ against pK_a^M. Similar tables for acetic acid can be found in the literature.*

TABLE 3.3

Comparison of the experimentally determined constants (pK_a^M) and the thermodynamic constant (pK_a^T) of β-naphthol at 20°

1	2	3	4	5
Concen-tration M	Ionic strength (I_m)	pK_a^M	pK_a^T	Δ
0·02214	0·01107	9·583	9·632	0·049
0·04164	0·02082	9·566	9·631	0·065
0·06100	0·03050	9·555	9·632	0·077
0·08022	0·04011	9·545	9·631	0·086
0·09928	0·04964	9·539	9·633	0·094
0·14628	0·07314	9·521	9·631	0·110
0·19240	0·09620	9·511	9·631	0·120
			Result: 9·632 ± 0·001	

Table 3.4, which relates I to $0·5\sqrt{I}$, may assist in the

* e.g. HARNED and EHLERS, *J. Amer. Chem. Soc.*, 1932, **54**, 1350.

interconversion of published pK_a^M into pK_a^T values, and vice versa, for purposes of comparison.

TABLE 3.4

Values of $0.5\sqrt{I}$

I	$0.5\sqrt{I}$
0·0050	0·03
0·0025	0·02
0·0010	0·02
0·0005	0·01

Activity corrections in acidic solutions

Case A (*b*) on p. 60 requires some amplification. For an example, we shall discuss a weak monoacidic base where the hydrogen ion term is comparable in magnitude to $[BH^+]_{Stoi}$. However the same treatment can be applied to titrations of monobasic acids, and it is valid both for hydrogen ion or hydroxyl ion corrections (see p. 31). Our treatment consists essentially of converting the $\{H^+\}$ or $\{OH^-\}$ terms, as used in corrections, to true concentrations in order to obtain more accurate values for $[A^-]$ and $[BH^+]$ which then undergo correction to activities.

The mass action equation may be rewritten (after reference to equations (1.6) and (2.4, *d*)):

$$pK_a^M = pH + \log \frac{[HCl] - [H^+]}{[Y] - [HCl] + [H^+]} \qquad (3.13)$$

where [Y] is the total concentration of unknown base originally present. From (3.13), and (3.14) which is the form of (3.2) applicable to bases, viz.:

$$K_a^T = \frac{\{H^+\}\{B\}}{\{BH^+\}} \qquad (3.14)$$

and the definition of pH given in equation (3.9), we obtain:

$$pK_a^T = pH + \log \frac{([HCl] - \{H^+\}/f_\pm^{1:1}) . f_+^{1:1}}{[Y] - [HCl] + \{H^+\}/f_\pm^{1:1}} \qquad (3.15)$$

It is evident that the ionic strength at any given point in the titration is $[BH^+]_{Real}$, in other words: $[HCl] - \{H^+\}/f_{\pm}^{1:1}$.

Before a value is assigned to this $[BH^+]$, it is necessary to obtain a value of $f_{\pm}^{1:1}$ to convert $\{H^+\}$, as measured, to $[H^+]$. This requires knowledge of the ionic strength which must be obtained by successive approximations, as follows:

The first approximation is to make

$$I_1 = [HCl] - \{H^+\} \tag{3.16}$$

then equation (3.7) is adapted as follows,

$$-\log f_{\pm}^{1:1} = \frac{0 \cdot 505 \sqrt{I_1}}{1 + 1 \cdot 6\sqrt{I_1}} \tag{3.17}$$

and hence

$$[H^+]_1 = \{H^+\}/f_{\pm}^{1:1} \tag{3.18}$$

Similarly, $I_2 = [HCl] - [H^+]_1$, and by using the same calculations, values of $[H^+]_2$ may be obtained and hence a third approximation of the ionic strength, I_3. The latter is taken as equal to $[BH^+]$ and is used to calculate a final value for $f_{\pm}^{1:1}$ in order to solve equation (3.15).

These calculations take a great deal of time. Fortunately there is an empirically derived approximation, suitable for results obtained with a pH set calibrated in 0·02 pH units:

$$pK_a^T = pH + \log \frac{[BH^+]_{Stoi} \cdot f_{\pm}^{1:1} - \{H^+\}}{[B]_{Stoi} + \{H^+\}} \tag{3.19}$$

where $f_{\pm}^{1:1}$ can be obtained from equation (3.17). Thus only a small amount of calculation is necessary in addition to that used in Table (2.6) (the titration of *p*-chloroaniline). Two extra columns should be added to those used in Table (2.6): the first to give the total concentration of base allowing for volume changes caused by the addition of the titrant, and the second to give values of $[BH^+]_{Stoi} \cdot f_{\pm}^{1:1}$.

The following figures permit comparison of pK_a^T values calculated alternatively by equations (3.15) and (3.19), at two different concentrations (each result represents the mean of nine values).

Conc. (M)	pK_a^T from (3.15)	pK_a^T from (3.19)
0·05	2·43 ± 0·01	2·44 ± 0·02
0·02	2·44 ± 0·03	2·44 ± 0·02

Let us consider a still weaker univalent base, one of pK_a^T 1·30, titrated at a concentration of 0·05M. The error caused by using the approximation (3.19) is 0·03 with reference to the pK_a^T as calculated by equation (3.15). This error is no greater than that produced by an error of 0·01 pH in reading the pH set. We have had much experience with equation (3.19) and we recommend it whenever the pH is measured with an instrument calibrated in units larger than 0·005 pH.

Activity corrections for divalent acids and bases

The following is an amplification of case A(*c*) on p. 60. The thermodynamic pK_a of the weaker group of a diacidic base (or of a dibasic acid) may be calculated from the equations:

$$pK_a^T = pH + \log \frac{[BH_2^{2+}]}{[BH^+]} - 3 \log f_\pm^{1:1} \quad \text{(for bases)} \quad (3.20, a)$$

$$\text{and} \quad pK_a^T = pH + \log \frac{[HA^-]}{[A^{2-}]} + 3 \log f_\pm^{1:1} \quad \text{(for acids)} \quad (3.20, b)$$

Using the definition of mixed constants (K_a^M) given on p. 58, it follows that $pK_a^T = pK_a^M \pm 3 \log f_\pm^{1:1}$ (positive sign for acids, negative sign for bases). The activity coefficient ($f_\pm^{1:1}$) is calculated by equation (3.17), and the ionic strength, following equation (3.5), is calculated, e.g. for bases, as:

$$I = 3[BH^{2+}] + [BH^+] \quad (3.21)$$

The results obtained by titrating the weaker basic group of ethylenediamine are shown in Table 3.5 and illustrate the validity of equation (3.20, *a*).

As a check, values of $\dfrac{\sqrt{I}}{1 + 1·6\sqrt{I}}$ and of pK_a^M were submitted to the method of least squares (see p. 163), and gave a mean slope of 1·49 (expected from theory: 1·51), from which identical pK_a^T values were calculated.

In Table 3.5, Δ is the difference between each pK_a^M value and the mean pK_a^T value.

If $\{H^+\}$ is relatively large, and the total concentration of unknown base does not exceed 0·03M, the more complex expression (3.22) is required to calculate pK_a^T:

$$pK_a^T = pH + \log \frac{[HCl]_2 - \{H^+\}/f_\pm^{1:1}}{Y - [HCl]_2 + \{H^+\}/f_\pm^{1:1}} - 3 \log f_\pm^{1:1} \quad (3.22)$$

where $[HCl]_2$ is the concentration of hydrochloric acid additional to the first equivalent used to obtain the pK_a of the stronger group, and Y is the original concentration of substance corrected for all volume changes due to the addition of titrant. The correct value of the ionic strength must be obtained by successive approximations in a similar way to that described on p. 63. The first approximation is $I_1 = 2([HCl] - \{H^+\}) + Y$.

TABLE 3.5

Comparison of mixed and thermodynamic ionization constants for the titration of the second step of a diacidic base

Example: ethylenediamine (20°)

Ionic strength I	Term for calculating mean ionic activity coefficient* $\dfrac{\sqrt{I}}{1 + 1·6\sqrt{I}}$	pK_a^M	pK_a^T	Δ
0·00500	0·0635	7·136	7·042	0·096
0·01486	0·1020	7·192	7·040	0·152
0·02450	0·1252	7·222	7·036	0·182
0·04326	0·1561	7·272	7·040	0·232
0·06132	0·1774	7·304	7·040	0·264
0·07870	0·1936	7·328	7·040	0·288
0·09546	0·2067	7·348	7·041	0·308

Result: $pK_a^T = 7·040 \pm 0·004$ at 20°.

* $-3 \log f_\pm^{1:1} = 1·51 \times$ this term.

Non-aqueous solvents

The order of relative strengths of a series of bases in anhydrous acetic acid has been shown to parallel their order of strengths in water.* This result induced Hall to measure in acetic acid a number of those very weak bases which are too readily hydrolysed to be titrated potentiometrically in water. To the pK_a values was added 2·0 which was the average difference for those bases that could be titrated both in acetic acid and in water. The results tended to be inexact (e.g. pK_a +0·06 instead of −0·17 for *o*-nitroaniline at 25°), but they served to open up a territory which might otherwise remain unexplored, viz. weak bases lacking ultraviolet spectra (e.g. urea, pK_a +0·10).

For these determinations glacial acetic acid is the solvent, and the titration is carried out with perchloric acid, using a 'chloranil electrode' (solid tetrachloro-benzoquinhydrone). An instrument reading to pH −3, or its equivalent in volts (−0·28 v), is required. Some substances, such as thiourea, react with chloranil and hence are not accessible to this technique.

Mixed solvents

When a substance is poorly soluble in water, but highly soluble in a volatile solvent, it is natural to consider determining the ionization constant in a mixture of the two solvents, e.g. in 50% ethanol. This temptation should be resisted, for reasons which will shortly be discussed.

The practice stems largely from a series of papers by M. Mizutani† on 'The Dissociation of Weak Electrolytes in Dilute Alcohols'. It was found, as would be expected, that alcohols weaken both acids and bases: e.g. the pK_a of an acid was raised by about 1·0, and that of a base lowered by about 0·5 (max. 0·89, min. 0·30) in 60% methanol. Hall and Sprinkle‡ plotted the curves of pK_a against decreasing alcohol concentration from 97% to 10% ethanol for 18 amines aliphatic and aromatic. Various amines had different slopes, but in some cases satisfactory extrapolation to 0% alcohol was possible. They found that the average depression of pK_a by 50% ethanol was 0·54 (max. 0·88, min.

* HALL, *J. Amer. Chem. Soc.*, 1930, **52**, 5115.
† e.g. MIZUTANI, *Z. physik. Chem.*, 1925, **118**, 318, 327.
‡ HALL and SPRINKLE, *J. Amer. Chem. Soc.*, 1932, **54**, 3469.

0·26). The extrapolation of these somewhat hockey-stick shaped curves proved difficult when the amine was too insoluble to give values in 10% and 20% ethanol, because successful extrapolation depended very much on knowing these values.

Titrations in 50% acetone have revealed still higher depressions of pK_a (1·5 to 2·5 units),* although in one case the curves of a series of acids were found to be more parallel in this solvent, and easier to extrapolate, than in dilute alcohols.† The depression caused by 50% dioxan is even greater than that caused by 50% acetone.

It is often said that the comparison of the strength of a series of substances in a mixed solvent is valid if the substances are chemically related. This is true so long as results of great precision are not expected. Thus in Table 3.6 it can be seen that in aqueous

TABLE 3.6

pK_a values of some chemically related amines in dilute ethanol (25°)

	Ethanol (% by weight)				
	0	20	35	50	65
Aniline	4·64	4·42	4·16	3·92	3·80
Methylaniline	4·84	4·62	4·28	3·90	3·64
Dimethylaniline	5·01	4·75	4·30	3·81	3·50

(GUTBEZAHL and GRUNWALD, *J. Amer. Chem. Soc.*, 1953, **75**, 559.)

solvents of ever increasing ethanolic content, aniline and its N-methyl-derivatives become weaker bases. But the effect of the alcohol is least on the unmethylated substance with this paradoxical result: although methylation increases the basic strength in 0% to 35% alcohol, in more highly alcoholic solutions it decreases the basic strength. Dilute dimethylformamide, methyl cellosolve and other glycol derivatives cause this type of trouble also.

* PRING, *Trans. Farad. Soc.*, 1924, **19**, 705.
† CAVILL, GIBSON and NYHOLM, *J. Chem. Soc.*, 1949, 2466.

Irregularities are often encountered when two chemically related substances differ in liposolubility. This follows from the dependence of ΔpK_a (the difference between the pK_a of a substance in water and its pK_a in a partly aqueous solvent) on the distribution coefficients of the various species involved in the equilibrium,[*] thus:

$$\Delta pK_a = \log D_{H^+} + \log D_B - \log D_{BH^+} \qquad (3.23)$$

where D_X is the distribution coefficient of X between the two solvents (the more lipophilic the species, the higher the coefficient).

Thus the more lipophilic species can be surrounded by a cage of solvent molecules of low dielectric constant, while the ion is surrounded mainly by water molecules. When B is highly lipophilic and BH^+ is not, a large ΔpK_a can be expected. This value should pass through a maximum with increasing lipophilic nature because eventually even the ion must be more soluble in the solvent than in water. Such a maximum is seen in the series of benzologues: pyridine, acridine and 8,9-benzacridine where ΔpK_a is respectively 0·73, 1·49, and 0·54 (water — 50% alcohol).[†]

Acids behave similarly. Thus, in water benzoic acid is 4 times as strong as acetic acid, but in 20% alcohol only 2·5 times as strong, and in 50% alcohol they have the same strength.[‡]

Fortunately the widespread availability of ultraviolet spectrophotometers makes it possible to obtain the pK_a values of many sparingly soluble substances by spectral methods. As a result, recourse to mixed solvents is becoming rarer.

[*] KOLTHOFF, LINGANE and LARSON, *J. Amer. Chem. Soc.*, 1938, **60**, 2512.
[†] ALBERT, *The Acridines*. London: Edward Arnold, 1951.
[‡] GRUNWALD and BERKOWITZ, *J. Amer. Chem. Soc.*, 1951, **73**, 4939.

4

Determination of Ionization Constants by Spectrometry

The determination of ionization constants by ultraviolet or visible spectrophotometry is more time-consuming than by potentiometry. However, spectrometry is the ideal method when a substance is too insoluble for potentiometry, or when its pK_a value is particularly low or high (e.g. less than 1·5, or more than 11).

The operations required in the spectrometric method are,

(a) Preparation of the stock solution, and suitable dilutions of it in appropriate buffers,

(b) Search for pure spectra of the two ionic species involved in the equilibrium,

(c) Choice of a wavelength suitable for the determination (the 'analytical wavelength'),

(d) Search for an approximate value of the pK_a,

(e) Exact determination of the pK_a.

Apparatus

The apparatus required consists of a photoelectric spectrophotometer, recently recalibrated (for wavelength *and* optical density) and free from stray light above 220 $m\mu$; 1- and 4- cm. matched cells (quartz with covers); graduated flasks and pipettes. An instrument for the potentiometric determination of pH must be close at hand.

Manually operated spectrophotometers are particularly suitable for this type of work (we use Hilger's 'Uvispek' instrument). Many automatic instruments do not reproduce density readings accurately enough for determination of pK, but can help in shortening the time taken to find the analytical wavelength.

Buffers

The necessary buffer solutions are given in Table 4.1. These solutions are conveniently stored at 0·1M strength in glass-distilled water. For use, they are diluted to 0·01M and adjusted with N-potassium hydroxide, or hydrochloric acid, to the required pH. Usually about 100 ml. of a 0·01M buffer solution is required for each spectroscopic measurement. If buffers other than those in Table 4.1 are used, they should first be tested to make sure that they do not absorb greatly in the region under investigation.

No solutions should be stored in polythene containers, which usually liberate an optically absorbing plasticizer.

TABLE 4.1

Buffers, suitable for spectrophotometry

Substance	Capacity (useful pH range)
A. *Range for general use*	
Formic acid	3·2–4·4
Acetic acid	4·2–5·4
Potassium dihydrogen phosphate	6·5–7·7
Ammonia	8·6–9·8
Boric acid	8·6–9·8
Ethylamine	10·1–11·3
B. *Auxiliary range*	
N-Ethyl morpholine[a]	7·0–8·2
Ethylene diamine[b]	$\begin{cases} 6·6–7·8 \\ 9·3–10·5 \end{cases}$
'Tris' (aminotrishydroxymethyl methane)[c]	7·5–8·7

[a] b.p. 138–139°. Commercial material may contain benzene, removable as a forerun in fractionation.
[b] The monohydrate, b.p. 118°, is commercially available.
[c] The pure solid is commercially available.

When working at a pH that falls between the capacity of two consecutive buffers, the solution should be made 0·01M with respect to *both* buffers. Thus, a mixture of acetic acid and potassium dihydrogen phosphate (0·01M, in each component) forms a good buffer for the range 5·4–6·5. A gap of 1·5 units can be covered in this way with efficient buffering.

It should be borne in mind that the optical absorption of these solutions, although low, is not negligible, and below 300 mμ many of the solutions absorb quite strongly. Hence it is important to get precisely the same proportion of buffers to other aqueous solutions in both optical cells. For example, if the first dilution of the unknown consists of 98 parts of buffer and 2 parts of aqueous stock solution, the comparison cell should contain a solution of buffer similarly diluted, 98 : 2, with water.

It is also important to note that the absorption of the solutions in Table 4.1 changes with the pH. Hence the pH of the contents of both optical cells must be identical to 0·03 unit, and it is advisable to check this once more after the optical density has been measured.

For pH values outside the range given in Table 4.1, hydrochloric acid and sodium or potassium hydroxide are used (see the concentration columns in Appendix I). These are described as 'solutions of known p[H$^+$]' as they lack buffering capacity. It is inadvisable to leave solutions of pH 13 in quartz cells for more than half an hour, but solutions of higher pH may be used in glass cells at such wavelengths as glass transmits.*

The acidity function

Hammett's discovery of the acidity function (H$_0$) provides an extension into regions of very high acidity.† The solutions of sulphuric acid in Table 4.2 serve as the equivalents of solutions of known pH for these highly acid regions. For determining the ionization constants of very weak uncharged bases, solutions of known H$_0$ take the place of the solutions of known p[H$^+$] mentioned above.‡ It is possible that in more acidic solutions these

---

* Solutions of known 'alkalinity function' up to the equivalent of pH 19, can be prepared from potassium hydroxide (SCHWARZENBACH and SULZBERGER, *Helv. chim. Acta*, 1944, **27**, 348).

† HAMMETT, *Physical Organic Chemistry*. New York: McGraw-Hill, 1940.
‡ BASCOMBE and BELL, *J. Chem. Soc.*, 1959, 1096.

two functions (H_0 and $p[H^+]$) diverge, but no serious theoretical or experimental difficulties have yet been encountered.

The H_0 scale was first constructed by measuring the ratio $[BH^+]/[B]$ for *p*-nitroaniline (the pK_a of which is known) in solutions of increasing acidity. When this ratio became high, a less basic indicator was substituted; its pK_a was calculated by measuring the $[BH^+]/[B]$ ratio in a solution of which the H_0 had been determined with *p*-nitroaniline, and similar measurements, with overlapping indicators, in solutions of ever-increasing acidity, finally enabled the calibrated scale to extend to H_0 −13. This scale is ideally suited to the determination of the pK values of other uncharged bases; it is unsuitable for the second pK of an ionized base. For the pK of a strong acid the requisite acidity function (H_-) can be obtained in acidic solutions standardized for this purpose.*

TABLE 4.2

Solutions of known acidity function (H_0)*

H_2SO_4	H_0	H_2SO_4	H_0
0·001N	3·03	8·58N	−2·03
0·01	2·08	9·22	−2·22
0·13	1·06	10·18	−2·45
1·08	0·09	11·4	−2·7
1·80	−0·23	12·7	−3·1
2·36	−0·42	14·1	−3·6
3·08	−0·64	15·3	−4·2
4·08	−0·90	70% w/w	−5·5
5·22	−1·20	80	−6·8
6·04	−1·42	85	−7·6
7·10	−1·68	95	−8·7

* BASCOMBE and BELL, *J. Chem. Soc.*, 1959, 1096; PAUL and LONG, *Chem. Rev.*, 1957, **57**, 1.

Equation for determining pK_a

Measurements of extinction coefficients are required to solve

* PHILLIPS, *Aust. J. Chem.*, 1961, **14**, 183.

equation (4.1). To obtain a reliable result it is advisable to solve it for at least seven different degrees of neutralization.

$$pK = pH \pm \log \frac{\varepsilon_I - \varepsilon}{\varepsilon - \varepsilon_M} \qquad (4.1)$$

Where ε_I is the extinction coefficient of the ion at the analytical wavelength, ε_M is the extinction coefficient of the molecule at the same wavelength, and ε is the extinction coefficient of the mixture of ion and molecule at the same wavelength. ε changes with the pH, which must be varied to solve the equation at various degrees of ionization.

Provided that the same concentrations and cell-thicknesses are used, equation (4.1) may be written with optical densities (d) replacing extinction coefficients (ε). This gives equation (4.2), which it is convenient to write in different forms to suit different needs.

When the functional group being determined is an acid, equation (4.2a) is used if d_I is greater than d_M, and (4.2b) if the reverse is the case.

$$pK_a = pH + \log \frac{d_I - d}{d - d_M} \qquad (4.2a)$$

$$pK_a = pH + \log \frac{d - d_I}{d_M - d} \qquad (4.2b)$$

When the group being determined is a base, equation (4.3a) is used if d_I is greater than d_M, and (4.3b) if the reverse is the case.

$$pK_a = pH + \log \frac{d - d_M}{d_I - d} \qquad (4.3a)$$

$$pK_a = pH + \log \frac{d_M - d}{d - d_I} \qquad (4.3b)$$

Thus the method consists of determining the relative proportions of ion to molecule in the unknown when it is dissolved in a series of solutions of accurately known pH values. This is done at a wavelength (called the analytical wavelength) at which the greatest difference in optical densities between ion and molecule is observed (e.g. 358 mμ in Fig. 4.1).

73

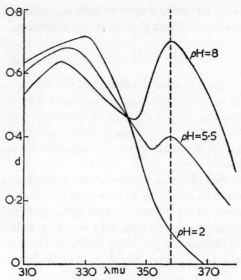

Fig. 4.1. Example of the determination of pK by spectrophotometry, showing the spectrum of the anion (pH 8), the spectrum of the neutral molecule (pH 2), and one (pH 5·5) of a series of spectra containing both species. For an analytical wavelength, 358 mμ was selected

Fig. 4.1 provides data for an acid undergoing determination of pK. The curve marked 'pH 8' is the spectrum of the anion free from other species, the curve marked 'pH 2' is the spectrum of the neutral molecule free from other species, and the curve marked 'pH 5·5' is one of a series of curves containing both species. At the analytical wavelength, the anion has d 0·700, the molecule has d 0·105, and the mixture at pH 5·5 has d 0·395. Thus equation (4.2) can be solved for pH 5·5.

Preparation of the stock solution of the unknown

If solubility permits and the extinction coefficient is not unusually low, a convenient strength for a stock solution is 5×10^{-4}M. (However, substances of high extinction coefficient have given pKs with a precision of ± 0.02 when poor solubility dictated that stock solutions as weak as 2×10^{-5}M be used.) To facilitate dissolution, an acidic compound may be dissolved in 0·005N-potassium hydroxide (if the pK_a is believed to lie below 10), and conversely a basic compound may be dissolved in 0·005N-hydrochloric acid (if the pK is believed to lie above 4). The good wetting properties of alcohol sometimes indicate its use for a concentrated primary solution, but the alcohol content must not exceed 1% in the final stock solution.

The search for the spectra of two pure ionic species

If the unknown is an acid, two spectra are required: that of the anion and that of the molecule. The stock solution is diluted to 10^{-4}M in 0·01N-hydrochloric acid and 0·01N-potassium hydroxide (i.e. at approximately pH 2 and 12 respectively). The optical density is then measured over the whole spectrum. The spectrum obtained in acid is that of the neutral molecule and the other is that of the anion. To see if either of these is an impure spectrum (i.e. if it contains the other ionic species) the unknown is again examined in 0·1N-hydrochloric acid and 0·1N-potassium hydroxide (i.e. at pH 1 and 13). If there is no change greater than 1% in the density of any peak, the two species may be considered to be isolated. If there is a change, the measurements should be repeated yet one pH unit further from neutrality.

The possibility of the following irregularities should be borne in mind,

(*a*) Both species may have the same spectrum, although this is uncommon,

(*b*) The substance may be decomposed by the acid or alkali: If so, an alteration in optical density with time should be noticed. If this is found, an attempt should be made to isolate the decomposing species nearer to neutrality, or an equation like (4·3*c*) can be used to obtain the optical density of this species, (*c*) The substance may have more than one ionizing group, and the two pure species isolated may differ not by one unit of charge, but by two. If this is the case, it will almost certainly be discovered during the search for the analytical wavelength (see below).

Accuracy at this stage in the determination of a pK requires that no more than 1% of one species should be present at the pH eventually chosen to record the spectrum of the other. Once the approximate pK is found, it is possible to see (from Appendix IV) whether these conditions were observed. If not, the determination should be repeated. Thus, for an acid, the anionic species must be determined not less than 2 pH units above the pK, and the molecular species not less than 2 pH units below the pK.

If the unknown is a base, the procedure is exactly the same as for an acid (see above). The spectrum obtained in acid is that of the cation, and that obtained in alkali is that of the molecule.

The choice of an analytical wavelength

Reference to Fig. 4.1 will show that when the curves of the two pure species are plotted, one particular wavelength can be found at which the two species differ most in density from one another. In Fig. 4.1. this lies at 358 mμ. Once this 'analytical wavelength' is chosen, the drum, or dial, of the spectrophotometer is set at this wavelength. It is most important that the drum should not be touched until all the measurements have been taken at the various pH values. Should the wavelength drum be moved to some other value temporarily, it cannot be reset *exactly* to the same value, and a minute difference in setting during a series of determinations can cause the results to fall outside the acceptable range of variation.

The ideal analytical wavelength is that at which one species absorbs strongly, and the other has no absorption at all. As this condition is rarely met, it is best to choose a wavelength where there is (i) a big difference in density between the species, and (ii) where in both species the density varies only slightly with changes

76

in wavelength.* These conditions should be sought (in decreasing order of preference) in,

   (*a*) A peak of one species over a trough in the other,
   (*b*) A peak over a peak, provided that there is a difference of 0·2 in the optical density readings,
   (*c*) A peak over a shoulder or inflection,
   (*d*) A trough over a trough.

At this stage, fresh solutions should be made up from stock, and the densities of both species redetermined at the analytical wavelength. This gives the d_I and d_M values for use in the final calculations. This is the stage at which to make sure that $10^{-4}M$ is actually the most suitable dilution, i.e. one that places both d_I and d_M values in the most sensitive density measuring range of the instrument.

Search for an approximate value of pK_a

The stock solution is diluted as before but into a buffer of such a pH that the unknown substance is only partly ionized. It is here that some knowledge of the ionization constants of common groups, and the effect on these constants of further substituents in the molecule, is valuable. This information can be obtained from Chapter 8. The density of this dilution is measured, and the pK calculated from the appropriate equation (4.2 or 4.3).

Exact determination of pK_a

Using this rough estimate of pK, seven buffer solutions are made at pH values numerically equal to this pK $+0, 0·2, 0·4, 0·6, -0·2, -0·4$ and $-0·6$ respectively. A set of seven values of pK are then obtained from measurements of the spectra of these solutions. The seven values are averaged as on p. 13. The spread should lie within $\pm0·06$ unit. If the spread is wider, the entire determination should be repeated (however, a higher spread, e.g. $\pm0·1$, is permissible when working at values below pK 0).

   With practice, the whole series of operations described above

* HISKEY, *Anal. Chem.*, 1949, **21**, 1440.

can be accomplished in one working day. If a recording spectro-photometer is used for the preliminary measurements, this time can be shortened.

Worked examples

Acridine has been selected as an example of a base the pK_a of which is appropriately obtained by spectrometry. The aqueous solubility at 20° is only 0·0003M, which is too dilute for potentiometric titration without special precautions (as on pp. 47, 60).

The stock solution of acridine was prepared as described in Table 4.3. To find a suitable analytical wavelength, 5 ml. of the stock solution was added to 5·0 ml. of 0·1N-HCl and diluted to

TABLE 4.3

Determination of the ionization constant of a monoacidic base

Substance: Acridine. $C_{13}H_9N$ = 179·21. *Temperature:* 20°.
Concentration: 0·0002M (2 × 10^{-4}M; M/5000). Recrystallized acridine, m.p. 110–111°, was dried overnight ($CaCl_2$, 20 mm., 20°), and 0·0896 g. was dissolved in 10 ml. of 0·1N-HCl and diluted to 250 ml. with glass-distilled water. This stock solution (0·002M in acridine and 0·004M in HCl) was diluted tenfold as indicated in the text.
Analytical wavelength: 403 mμ. *Cells:* 1 cm.
Optical density of neutral molecule (d_M) = 0·025.
Optical density of cation (d_I) = 0·608.

1	2	3	4	5	6
pH	d	$d_I - d$	$d - d_M$	$\log \dfrac{d - d_M}{d_I - d}$	pK_a (= pH + column 5)
6·30	0·125	0·483	0·100	−0·68	5·62
6·10	0·170	0·438	0·145	−0·48	5·62
5·89	0·235	0·373	0·210	−0·25	5·64
5·68	0·299	0·309	0·274	−0·05	5·63
5·47	0·367	0·241	0·342	+0·15	5·62
5·27	0·429	0·179	0·404	+0·36	5·63
5·08	0·474	0·134	0·449	+0·53	5·61
4·85	0·523	0·085	0·498	+0·77	5·62

Result: pK_a = 5·62 ± 0·02, at 20° and I = 0·01 (using all eight values in the set).

50 ml. with water. This solution was 0·0002M with respect to acridine, in 0·01N-HCl (pH 2). The optical density of this solution was measured (in 1-cm. cells) over a series of wavelengths using 0·01N-HCl in the blank cell. A maximum ($d = 0·608$) was found at 403 mμ. The same result was obtained in 0·1N-HCl (pH 1), hence it was concluded that this peak represents the cation. The neutral molecule was found to have only a low absorption at this wavelength ($d = 0·025$ both at pH 9·1 and pH 13), and its λ_{max} is at a lower wavelength. Hence 403 mμ was selected for the analytical wavelength.

Next, a sighting reading was obtained by diluting 5 ml. of the

TABLE 4.3, *a*

Determination of the ionization constant of a weak monoacidic base

Substance: *p*-Nitroaniline. $C_6H_6N_2O_2 = 138·12$. *Temperature:* 20°.
Concentration: 0·0001M. Recrystallized material was dried overnight (CaCl$_2$, 20 mm., 20°) and 0·0691 g. was dissolved in 500 ml. of glass-distilled water to give a 10^{-3}M stock solution, which was diluted tenfold with the solutions of hydrochloric acid given in column 1, below.
Analytical wavelength: 270 mμ. *Cells:* 1 cm.
Optical density of neutral molecule (d_M) = 0·138 (pH 4·7).
Optical density of cation (d_I) = 0·693 (pH −1·68).

1	1*a*	2	3	4	4*a*	5	6
N-HCl	pH (calculated on 90% of column 1)		$d_I - d$	$d - d_M$	$\dfrac{d - d_M}{d_I - d}$	log of column 5	pK$_a$ (= pH + column 5)
0·0235	1·67	0·233	0·460	0·095	95/460	−0·68	0·99
0·0373	1·47	0·276	0·417	0·138	138/417	−0·48	0·99
0·0607	1·26	0·335	0·358	0·197	197/358	−0·26	1·00
0·0969	1·06	0·400	0·293	0·262	262/293	−0·05	1·01
0·1485	0·87	0·462	0·231	0·324	324/231	+0·15	1·02
0·234	0·67	0·522	0·171	0·384	384/171	+0·35	1·02
0·373	0·47	0·570	0·123	0·432	432/123	+0·55	1·02

Result: pK$_a$ (thermodynamic) = 1·01 ± 0·02 at 20° (using all seven values in the set).

Ionization Constants

stock solution to 50 ml. with phosphate–acetate buffer (0·01M) previously adjusted to pH 5·5. The measured pH of the solution was found to be 5·47 and the optical density was 0·367 (at 403 mμ). Hence pK_a = 5·62 (from the formula in column 6 of Table 4.3). From this approximate value, the following steps led to a set of seven values. Eight solutions, all 0·0002M in acridine, were prepared by tenfold dilution of the stock solution with buffers to give a series of pH values spaced fairly evenly through a range of 1·4 pH units, viz.: 0·7 units above and below the pH numerically equal to the approximate pK_a. The pH and optical densities of

TABLE 4.4

Determination of the ionization constant of a monobasic acid

Substance: 8-Hydroxyquinoline. C_9H_7NO = 145·15. *Temperature:* 20°.
Concentration: 0·00005M. Recrystallized material was dried overnight (CaCl$_2$, 20 mm., 20°), and 7·26 mg. was dissolved in 500 ml. of glass-distilled water to give a 0·0001M stock solution. This was diluted twofold with various buffers.
Analytical wavelength: 355 mμ (the neutral molecule has λ_{max} 300 mμ).
  Cells: 4 cm.
Optical density of neutral molecule (d_M) = 0·045 (pH 7·5).
Optical density of anion (d_I) = 0·558 (pH 13).

1	2	3	4	5	6
pH	d	$d_I - d$	$d - d_M$	$\log \dfrac{d_I - d}{d - d_M}$	pK_a (= pH + column 5)
9·12	0·123	435	78	+0·75	9·87
9·32	0·167	391	122	+0·51	9·83
9·52	0·216	342	171	+0·30	9·82
9·65	0·243	315	198	+0·20	9·85
9·89	0·310	248	265	−0·03	9·86
10·12	0·370	188	325	−0·24	9·88
10·28	0·415	143	370	−0·41	9·87
10·53	0·465	93	420	−0·65	9·88

Result: pK_a = 9·86 ± 0·04, at 20° and I = 0·01 (using all eight values in the set). (cf. pK_a = 9·89 ± 0·03 determined potentiometrically at 0·005M; ALBERT, *Biochem. J.*, 1953, **54**, 646.)

these solutions were then measured giving the set of values shown in Table 4·3. These values were then averaged (as on p. 13) to give the required result. Another spectrometric determination of the ionization constant of a base is given in Table 4·3, *a*. The substance, *p*-nitroaniline, has too low a pK_a for potentiometric titration (it is 1·01), but is very conveniently handled by this method.

The spectrometric determination of the ionization constant of an acid, carried out similarly, is exemplified in Table 4.4. The example chosen (8-hydroxyquinoline) is soluble enough, and a strong enough acid, to be determined potentiometrically with considerable saving of time. However, it is interesting to compare results obtained by the two methods, and this is done in the last line of Table 4.4.

8-Hydroxyquinoline is an amphoteric substance, and there is a basic pK_a at 5·13. However, the two pKs are well spaced (see p. 149) and do not interfere with the use of either method.

Precision, accuracy, and activity corrections

The spectrometric method, carefully performed, yields results of high precision. The set of seven values, obtained over a range of 1·5 units of pH, should be rejected unless the average result falls within the range $\pm 0·06$; with practice this spread can be reduced.* It is not practicable to extend the set to nine values over a range of 1·9 pH units, as is recommended in potentiometric titration (p. 28), because the two new end values would be too sensitive to small instrumental errors.

Precision can be heightened by replacing the covered cells by the more expensive stoppered cells. In this way evaporation and ingress of carbon dioxide can be minimized.

If temperature is controlled by a jacketed cell-holder, results of high *accuracy* are obtainable comparable with those given by any other method. But as this precaution is only beginning to be widely observed, the accuracy of published results obtained by spectrometry is usually less than what the precision may suggest. Variation of pK_a with small changes in temperature is a property of

* But $\pm 0·1$ is allowable for results below pK 0.

bases, phenols, the hydroxyl ion and many buffers such as borate (see p. 172).

No corrections for hydrogen ions or hydroxyl ions enter into the spectrometric method, because stoicheiometric concentrations are avoided by direct optical measurement of the real concentrations.

Because the unknown is present at such great dilution, it might be assumed that the pK_a values obtained by the spectrometric method are thermodynamic. This is not so because of the presence of buffer salts. Thus the results are 'mixed pK_a values' as defined on p. 58 and the concentration to be used in any activity corrections is that of the buffer salts used (usually 0·01M).

Conversion to thermodynamic pK values can be made by consideration of the ionic strength of each solution, as described on p. 59. When the buffers are uni-univalent (e.g. sodium acetate) and do not exceed 0·01M, there is very little difference between the two kinds of pK. But when polyvalent ions are concerned, the difference is somewhat greater (see p. 64), unless the polyvalence concerns opposite charges as in glycine (see p. 119).

When acidity function (H_0) solutions are used to obtain the pK_a of a *mono*acidic base, the results are thermodynamic pK_a values. This is also the case when known *concentrations* of hydrogen ions are used (e.g. the use of 0·02N-hydrochloric acid to give $p[H^+]$ 1·70, without reference to potentiometry, see Appendix I). The reason is that:

$$K_a^T = \frac{[H^+]\,[B]}{[BH^+]} \cdot \frac{f_{H^+} \cdot f_B}{f_{BH^+}}$$

In so far as f_B is taken as 1, and f_{H^+} as equalling f_{BH^+} (see mean ionic activity coefficients, p. 59), it follows that $K_a^T = K_a^C$. This fortunate dispensation does not apply to acids, where f_{H^+} and f_{A^-} have to be multiplied.

Common sources of error

The commonest error is to use the spectrometric method when the much quicker potentiometric method would suffice (the limitations of potentiometry with the glass electrode are outlined on p. 27).

Imprecision in a set of results can usually be traced to one of the following causes:

(*a*) The buffers solutions were used in the spectrophotometer at a different temperature from that at which their pH values were measured,

(*b*) The solvent in the blank cell (compensation cell) had not exactly the same composition as that used for the unknown (see p. 71),

(*c*) The wavelength drum was reset during the course of the measurements (see p. 76),

(*d*) The two spectrophotometer cells were not a matched pair.

Refinements of the spectrometric method

The spectrometric method can be modified for some difficult cases. Weak acids (i.e. those with pK $>$11) do not give a consistent set of results in the ordinary way because the pH of the buffers are measured in a region where the glass electrode is not reliable. Below, we give a graphical treatment which compensates for the error introduced in this way, and enables the spectrometric method to be used with reliance in the highly alkaline region. This is followed by a method for measuring two pK values which are near enough to ionize simultaneously and thus cause mutual interference. Finally an indicator method is outlined which is occasionally used for the spectrometric determination of pK_a in those substances which give no spectrum.

(a) *The pK_a of a very weak acid (graphical treatment).* Sometimes a particular ionic species cannot be isolated because it decomposes, or because the solution would be too alkaline for accurate work. In such cases (the last named often arises with acids of pK_a $>$11) equations (4.2*a*) and (*b*), or equations (4.3*a*) and (*b*), can be rearranged to yield straight-line relationships which lead to the desired pK_a.

Table 4.5 illustrates this method by the determination of the

Ionization Constants

TABLE 4.5

Example of the graphical treatment of spectrometric data to find the ionization constant of a very weak acid

Substance: Salicylic acid (phenolic group). *Temperature:* 20°C.
Concentration: 0·001M. Recrystallized material (AR) was dried overnight ($CaCl_2$, 20 mm. 20°), and a stock solution in water (0·005M) was diluted fivefold in the presence of sodium hydroxide and sodium chloride, as on p. 85.
Analytical wavelength: 330 mμ.
Optical density of mono-anion = 0·123 at 330 mμ (pH 9·2). *Cells:* 1 cm.

1	2	3	4	5	6	7
[NaOH] (by titration)	$[H^+]$	pH	$d - d_{A^-}$	$[H^+](d - d_{A^-})$	d	pK_a^C
1·226	$0·555 \times 10^{-14}$	14·26	1·013	$5·622 \times 10^{-15}$	1·136	13·85
0·681	0·999	14·00	0·857	8·561	0·980	13·81
0·347	1·965	13·71	0·633	12·438	0·756	13·80
0·135	5·059	13·30	0·337	17·049	0·460	13·80
0·068	10·012	13·00	0·176	17·621	0·299	13·85

Intercept, when $[H^+](d - d_A-) = 0$, is 1·535, $= d_{A^2-}$.
Result: $pK_a^C = 13·82 \pm 0·03$ at an ionic strength of 1·226.

pK_a of the phenolic group in salicylic acid (pK_a 13·82). The lower (carboxylic) pK_a is 3·00. The spectrum of the mono-anion was determined (at pH 9·2), and other spectra in 0·681N-NaOH and in 1·226N-NaOH. All three spectra proved to be different and it was inexpedient to use stronger alkali for several reasons, of which the principal reason is the high absorption of light by the hydroxyl ion. Thus it was evident that a pure spectrum of the di-anion could not be isolated for use in the usual calculations. Hence a 'graphical' treatment was adopted.

The analytical wavelength (330 mμ) was chosen in the usual way (p. 76). Solutions (0·001M) of salicylic acid were prepared in the molarities of sodium hydroxide (carbonate-free) shown in column 1. The ionic strength of the solutions was equalized by adding sodium chloride to four of them so that $I = 1\cdot226$. The optical densities of these solutions are given in column 6. Because $d_{A^{2-}}$, the density of the di-anion, is not directly obtainable, equation (4.2a) was rearranged as follows:

$$K_a^C = [H^+]\left(\frac{d - d_{A^-}}{d_{A^{2-}} - d}\right),$$

whence

$$d = d_{A^{2-}} - \frac{[H^+](d - d_{A^-})}{K_a^C} \qquad (4.3c)$$

The hydrogen ion concentration $[H^+]$ was calculated from $K_w/[NaOH]$. Finally the method of least squares (see p. 163) was applied to the values of d and of $[H^+](d - d_{A^-})$. This operation gave $1\cdot535$ as the optical density of the di-anion. Using this mean value of the intercept, the values of the 'concentration pK_a' at an ionic strength of $1\cdot226$ were calculated.

(b) *Overlapping pK_a values.* When a substance has two ionizing groups that lie within 3 pK units of one another, interference is experienced in the determination of the pK values. How this difficulty arises, and how it is overcome in the potentiometric method, was described on p. 52. In the spectrometric method, little difficulty is encountered if an analytical wavelength can be found where the uncharged and the doubly charged species have an identical absorbance which differs from that of the singly charged species.* But in some cases such an analytical wavelength cannot be found, a state of affairs which is commonest in highly symmetrical molecules. Benzidine (I) provides an example of how this difficulty can be tackled, although each substance may pose its own problems depending on the nature of the spectra.

$$H_2N-\!\!\bigcirc\!\!-\!\!\bigcirc\!\!-NH_2 \quad (C_{12}H_{12}N_2 = 184\cdot23)$$

(I)

The spectrum of the molecular species of benzidine was obtained at pH 9, and was found to be repeatable at pH 7 without any

---

* KOK-PENG ANG, *J. Phys. Chem.*, 1958, **62**, 1109; THAMER and VOIGT. ibid., 1952, **56**, 225.

change in optical density. Similarly, the spectrum of the di-cation was measured at pH 1, and no change was observed at pH 0. The pH range, within which optical densities occur, differing slightly from those observed at the maxima of the pure molecular and dicationic species, was found to be 5·5 to 2·7. Thus ionization of the two basic groups must occur within this pH range. Four complete spectra, ranging from 350 to 215 mμ, were then determined at pH 5·4, 4·7, 4·1 and 3·4. From these spectra a tentative choice of analytical wavelengths could be made viz.: 300 and 235–245 mμ. The following reasons governed the choice:

(*a*) At 300 mμ the molecular species absorbed strongly and the di-cation had zero absorption,

TABLE 4.6

Variation of optical densities of benzidine with pH

Concentration: 5 × 10⁻⁵M.
Cells: 1 cm.
Temperature: 20°C.

pH	Optical density	
	d_1 at 300 mμ	d_2 at 245 mμ
7·10	0·822	0·262
5·40	0·766	0·260
5·30	0·755	0·260
5·14	0·726	0·260
4·92	0·685	0·263
4·72	0·637	0·278
4·56	0·597	—
4·32	0·531	—
4·10	0·455	—
3·91	0·380	0·485
3·74	0·321	0·559
3·54	0·255	0·628
3·30	0·181	0·726
3·12	0·136	0·774
3·00	0·110	0·808
2·88	0·088	0·835
1·00	0·000	0·940

(b) In the range 235 to 245 mμ the optical density remained fairly constant from pH 7 to 4·7, indicating that the mono-cation and molecule could have equal absorbance at some wavelength within this range. Furthermore a maximum in the spectra of the di-cation is observed in this range.

Fifteen solutions were made up in 0·01M buffers covering the pH range 5·4 to 2·9 as shown in Table 4·6. Measurements of their optical densities were made (with the same buffers adjusted to the same pH in the blank cell) at 300 mμ and 235–245 mμ. The optical density measured at 245 mμ did not vary in the pH range 7 to 4·92 and therefore this wavelength was chosen as the second analytical wavelength.

From these results, the two basic pK_a values can be calculated by a method of successive approximations as follows:

(a) First of all, the optical density tentatively assigned to the mono-cation (0·260) at 245 mμ had to be confirmed because the constant value obtained between pH 5·40 and 4·92 may be due to a cancellation of two equal effects. Thus the value for the mono-cation may be decreasing as the pH is lowered, but this decrease may be compensated exactly by an increase due to the formation of the di-cation in this pH range. The equation governing the ionization of the weaker basic group is

$$BH_2^{++} \rightleftharpoons BH^+ + H^+$$

Whence
$$K_{a2} = \frac{[H^+][BH^+]}{[BH_2^{++}]}$$

At 245 mμ,
$$K_{a2} = [H^+]\left(\frac{d_2^{II} - d_2}{d_2 - d_2^{I}}\right) \qquad (4.4)$$

where d_2^{II} is the optical density of pure di-cationic species = 0·940
    d_2 is the observed optical density at given values of [H$^+$],
and d_2^{I} is the unknown optical density of the pure mono-cation.
    Equation (4.4) rearranges to:

$$d_2 = \frac{[H^+]}{K_{a2}}(d_2^{II} - d_2) + d_2^{I} \qquad (4.5)$$

87

A graph, constructed by plotting d_2 against $[H^+](d_2^{II} - d_2)$ gives a straight line of slope $1/K_{a2}$ and intercept d_2^I. The intercept is 0·260 which agrees with the value provisionally assigned to the optical density of the mono-cation at 245 mμ. Using this value, pK_2 can be calculated for each of the seven values between pH 2·88 and 3·91 by

$$pK_{a2} = pH + \log\left(\frac{d_2 - 0·260}{0·940 - d_2}\right)$$

$$= 3·62 \pm 0·02$$

(b) Using this value of pK_{a2}, the optical density of the mono-cation at 300 mμ (d_1^I) can be calculated, but only as an approximation because the observed optical density between pH 3·00 and 3·91 (at 300 mμ) is due to the presence of all three species. Thus,

$$K_{a2} = \left(\frac{d_1 - d_1^{II}}{d_1^I - d_1}\right).[H^+] \tag{4.6}$$

Combining equations (4.4) and (4.6) using the same pH values, and rearranging gives:

$$d_1^I = d_1 + (d_1 - d_1^{II}).\left(\frac{d_2 - d_2^I}{d_2^{II} - d_2}\right) \tag{4.7}$$

where d_1 is the observed optical density at 300 mμ, d_1^{II} is the optical density of the di-cation at 300 mμ (0·000); d_2, d_2^I, d_2^{II} have the same values as were used in equation (4.4), all measured at 245 mμ.

Using six results of d_1 and d_2 at each wavelength (measured at identical pH values between 3·00 and 3·91), an approximate value of the optical density of the mono-cation at 300 mμ is obtained ($d_1^I = 0·566 \pm 0·011$).

(c) Knowing $d_1^I \simeq 0·566$ and $pK_2 = 3·62$, the observed optical densities (d_1) in the pH range 4·10 to 5·40 (where the ionization of the stronger basic group is occurring) can be corrected for the influence of the di-cation using the relationship:

Corrected optical density $d_1^c = \left(\dfrac{d_1^{obs} - \dfrac{\dfrac{K_{a2}.d_1^I}{[H^+]} + d_1^{II}}{1 + \dfrac{K_{a2}}{[H^+]}}\right) + d_1^I$ (4.8)

The expression
$$\left(\frac{\frac{K_{a2} . d_1^{I}}{[H^+]} + d_1^{II}}{1 + \frac{K_{a2}}{[H^+]}}\right)$$

arises directly from equation (4.6) and is the optical density calculated at the relevant pH values assuming that further ionization of the mono-cation is free from any interference due to the ionization of the neutral molecule. The difference between these calculated values and the observed optical densities (d_1) at the same pH values is therefore due to the presence of the neutral molecule. These differences, when added to the approximate value of the density of the mono-cation at 300 mμ (d_1^{I}), yield the optical densities which would be due to the ionization of free base without interference from the further ionization of the mono-cation. Using the seven values of the optical densities so corrected, and the value of d_1^{I}, an approximate value of pK_1 for the equilibrium:

$$BH^+ \rightleftharpoons B + H^+$$

can be obtained.

$$pK_1 = pH + \log\left(\frac{0.822 - d_1^{c}}{d_1^{c} - d_1^{I}}\right) \qquad (4.9)$$

whence $pK_1 \simeq 4.81$.

(*d*) The approximate value of K_1 is now used to correct the observed optical densities at 300 mμ and pH values between 3.00 and 3.91 for the influence of free base upon the ionization of the di-cation by means of the equation:

$$d_1^{c2} = d_1^{I} - \left(\left[\frac{\frac{K_1}{[H^+]} . d_1^{M} + d_1^{I}}{1 + \frac{K_1}{[H^+]}}\right] - d^{obs}\right) \qquad (4.10)$$

Where d_1^{M} is the optical density of the free base at 300 m$\mu = 0.822$.

(*e*) These values for d_1^{c2} are substituted for d_1 in equation (4.7) and the whole calculation procedure involving equations (4.8), (4.9) and (4.10) repeated until constant results are obtained. The

TABLE 4.7

The overlapping ionization constants of benzidine

Density values used: $d_1^M = 0.822$ (300 mμ); $d_1^{II} = 0.000$ (300 mμ). Temperature: 20°.
$d_2^I = 0.260$ (245 mμ); $d_2^{II} = 0.940$ (245 mμ).

Remarks	Eqn. used	pH	3·00	3·12	3·30	3·54	3·74	3·91	4·10	4·32	4·56	4·72	4·92	5·14	5·30	5·40	Mean values
		Obs. d_1 (300 mμ)	0·110	0·136	0·181	0·255	0·321	0·380	0·455	0·531	0·597	0·637	0·685	0·726	0·755	0·766	—
		Obs. d_2 (245 mμ)	0·808	0·774	0·726	0·628	0·559	0·485	—	—	—	—	—	—	—	—	—
First series of calculations; d_1^{c2} substituted in equation (4.7) to start second series	(4.7)	d_1^I (300 mμ)	0·567	0·557	0·575	0·556	0·573	0·568	—	—	—	—	—	—	—	—	0·566
	(4.8)	d_1^{rc} (corr.)	—	—	—	—	—	—	—	0·625	0·655	0·679	0·712	0·742	0·767	0·775	—
	(4.9)	pK_1	—	—	—	—	—	—	—	4·84	4·83	4·82	4·80	4·80	4·74	4·75	4·80
	(4.10)	d_2^{rc2} (corr.)	0·106	0·131	0·173	0·242	0·300	0·351	—	—	—	—	—	—	—	—	—
Second series of calculations; new values of d_1^2 substituted in equation (4.7) to start third series	(4.7)	d_1^I (300 mμ)	0·546	0·537	0·550	0·527	0·535	0·526	—	—	—	—	—	—	—	—	0·537
	(4.8)	d_1^{rc} (recorr.)	—	—	—	—	—	—	—	0·620	0·652	0·677	0·711	0·741	0·766	0·775	—
	(4.9)	pK_1	—	—	—	—	—	—	—	4·71	4·73	4·74	4·72	4·74	4·69	4·70	4·73 ±0·04
	(4.10)	d_2^{rc2} (recorr.)	0·105	0·129	0·170	0·238	0·295	0·343	—	—	—	—	—	—	—	—	—
Third series of calculations	(4.7)	d_1^I (300 mμ)	0·541	0·528	0·540	0·519	0·526	0·513	—	—	—	—	—	—	—	—	0·528
	(4.8)	d_1^{rc2} (further corr.)	—	—	—	—	—	—	0·586	0·619	0·651	0·676	0·710	0·741	0·766	0·775	—
	(4.9)	pK_1	—	—	—	—	—	—	4·70	4·67	4·70	4·72	4·71	4·72	4·67	4·68	4·70 ±0·03
	(4.10)	d_1^{rc2} (further corr.)	0·105	0·129	0·169	0·236	0·293	0·339	0·396	0·444	—	—	—	—	—	—	—
		pK_2 using values of d_1^{rc2}	3·61	3·61	3·63	3·63	3·65	3·66	3·62	3·61	—	—	—	—	—	—	3·63 ±0·03

Results: pK_1 = 4·70 ± 0·03; pK_2 = 3·63 ± 0·03, at 20°.

values are given in Table 4.7 and the final results for pK_1 and pK_2, calculated at 300 $m\mu$, are 4.70 ± 0.03 and 3.63 ± 0.03 respectively.

Spectrometric determination of the pK_a of substances lacking an absorption spectrum

In the general method, outlined in this chapter, optically transparent base-pairs (buffers) are added in great excess to the system being investigated so as to control the pH and hence the position of the acid–base equilibrium being studied. This method can also be applied in reverse, i.e. by adding optically opaque acid–base pairs (indicators) in such small amounts that they have no appreciable effect on the state of the system. The relative concentrations of ion and molecule in the indicator, as measured spectrometrically, reveal the pH of the system being investigated. This affords a method for the spectrometric determination of pK_a for substances lacking an absorption spectrum. The method is useful for pK_a values higher than 11, also for examining deuterated substances. In most other cases, potentiometric titration with the glass electrode is more accurate and convenient.

Nine solutions of the unknown acid are made up to contain such stoicheiometric concentrations of [HA] and [A⁻] as are given in Table 2.1. An indicator that changes colour in about half of these solutions is found by experimental sampling. This indicator is then added to each solution in exactly equal amounts, so as to give a final concentration of 0·00005M (for a 0·01M solution of the unknown). Optical densities of the indicator are then measured at the λ_{max} of each of the two species. (Bromophenol blue, for example, has these maxima at 440 and 600 $m\mu$ respectively.) The ratio of the densities (α) enables the values of pK_a to be calculated from the equation:

$$pK_a = pK_{ind} + \log[HA] - \log[A^-] - \log\alpha \qquad (4.11)$$

where pK_{ind} is the pK_a of the indicator, e.g. 4·22 for bromophenol blue.* The terms [HA] and [A⁻] need correction both for [H⁺] and

---

* KILPATRICK, *J. Amer. Chem. Soc.*, 1934, **56**, 2048. pK values of other indicators can be traced from this reference.

for the displacement of buffer ratio caused by converting one species of the indicator partly into the other. If the pH of the indicator is close to that of the unknown, these corrections may be quite small in practice.

5

Determination of Ionization Constants
by Conductimetry

The first ionization constants were determined by Ostwald very soon after Arrhenius discovered the phenomenon of ionization. Ostwald applied the law of mass action to the ionization of carboxylic acids at various dilutions. Using Kohlrausch's method to obtain the equivalent conductance (Λ_c), and Arrhenius's derivation of the degree of ionization (α) from equation (5.1), he substituted α in the mass law formula (as in equation 5·2) and obtained constants which varied only a little with dilution.

$$\alpha = \frac{\Lambda_c}{\Lambda_0} \tag{5.1}$$

$$K_a = \frac{\alpha^2 c}{1 - \alpha} \tag{5.2}$$

where K_a is the acidic ionization constant, α is the degree of ionization, Λ_c is the *equivalent conductance* and Λ_0 the *limiting conductance*.

Λ_c, the equivalent conductance, is the conductance of a solution containing one gram equivalent of the solute per gram or millilitre (both standards are in use) when placed between electrodes, each of 1 sq. cm., which are 1 cm. apart. For uni-univalent substances Λ_c is also the molecular conductance. The equivalent conductance increases, on dilution, to a limiting value which is Λ_0, the limiting conductance, or the 'conductance at infinite dilution'.

The high equivalent conductances of hydrogen and hydroxyl ions, respectively 325 and 179 (at 20°), arise from their not having to transport hydration shells as they move. Most other ions have equivalent conductances of only 40 to 70 (at 20°).

Scope of the method

Until 1932, conductimetry was the method most used for obtaining ionization constants. In that year, co-operative work showed that potentiometry* could yield results just as accurate as those obtain by conductimetry.† The test substance was acetic acid, and the results were $1 \cdot 754 \times 10^{-5}$ ($= pK_a$ $4 \cdot 756$) and $1 \cdot 753 \times 10^{-5}$ ($= pK_a$ $4 \cdot 756$) respectively, at 25°. Thereafter the potentiometric method rapidly gained in favour as it was found to be more versatile and quicker, and to require fewer calculations. Accordingly, when a critical list was published in 1939 of reliable ionization constants,‡ the only conductimetric constants found acceptable were those of acids, and all of these had pK_a values in the range $1 \cdot 89$ to $5 \cdot 15$. Within this narrow range, conductimetry long remained unequalled for work of the highest precision. Today conductimetry is much used for the determining of the ionization constants of very weak acids in the pK_a range of 11 to 14 (see below, p. 95). However, it is not so suitable for strong bases in this pK region, where special spectrometric and potentiometric methods (pp. 83, 49) are available for both acids and bases.

A conductimetric determination of pK_a differs particularly from the corresponding potentiometric determination in this way: the values in a set are obtained by simple dilution, and not by titration with acid or alkali at a fixed concentration. Hence conductimetric work is often in need of activity corrections and this can make the calculations (lengthy enough in themselves) quite tedious. Apart from this, the practical work is at least twice as time-consuming as in potentiometric titration because Λ_0 has to be obtained experimentally from a salt, as well as Λ_c from the free acid or base, before any value for pK_a can be worked out.

As ordinarily used, i.e. by successive dilutions of a solution of

---

* HARNED and EHLERS, *J. Amer. Chem. Soc.*, 1932, **54**, 1350.
† MacINNES and SHEDLOVSKY, *J. Amer. Chem. Soc.*, 1932, **54**, 1429.
‡ DIPPY, *Chem. Rev.*, 1939, **25**, 151.

the unknown substance, conductimetry does not give accurate results for any acid with pK_a over 6·5. This is because of the inevitable presence of some carbon dioxide in the water used. Whereas a stronger acid can suppress the ionization of carbonic acid ($pK_a = 6·5$) an acid with pK_a above 6·5 must necessarily have its ionization partly repressed by the carbonic acid. In any case, the ionization of very weak acids is too slight to produce a sufficient concentration of hydrogen ions for accurate measurement against the background of the natural conductivity of water. Thus for an acid of pK_a 9, a 0·1M solution is needed to obtain significant readings, for an acid of pK_a 8, a 0·01M solution, and so on: if these are the initial concentrations, significant readings cannot persist through many dilutions.

A more successful treatment of weak acids is to find how much they inhibit the conductivity of hydroxyl ions in a solution of sodium hydroxide. For example, the ionization constant of boric acid (pK 9·25) was successfully determined from the conductivity of solutions containing various proportions of ammonia and boric acid.* The more difficult case of trifluoroethanol (pK 12·37) was similarly dealt with by observing the conductivity of solutions containing varying proportions of this substance and sodium hydroxide.† It will be at once recognized that these are actually conductimetric titrations, a technique which suffers from two disadvantages, (*a*) a small amount of any strongly acidic impurity in the unknown acid introduces a large error, and (*b*) although the conductivity due to the hydroxyl ions is diminished by the unknown acid, the conductivity due to the sodium ions (which have no less than one-quarter of the conductivity of hydroxyl ions) remains throughout the titration (see Table 5.2).

Disadvantages. The almost inevitable exposure of the unknown substance to carbon dioxide has prevented conductimetry from being widely used for determining the ionization constants of bases. Conductimetry is not easily adapted to determining the second ionization constant in a substance with two ionizing

---

* LUNDÉN, *J. Chim. physique*, 1907, **5**, 574.
† BALLINGER and LONG, *J. Amer. Chem. Soc.*, 1959, **81**, 1050.

groups. Because of the high conductivity of salts, conductimetry is not suitable for determining ionization constants at constant

A special advantage of conductimetry is that significant results can be obtained at great dilution, provided that the acid has a sufficiently low pK_a. Thus Table 5.1 shows that an accurate value can still be obtained for acetic acid ($pK = 4\cdot76$) at $2\cdot8 \times 10^{-5}$M, a concentration at which potentiometry would require special apparatus and precautions (see pp. 48, 61).

Apparatus

Conductance is the reciprocal of resistance. Hence the first requirement is to measure the specific resistance of the solution, i.e.

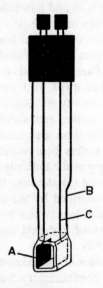

Fig. 5.1. Electrode unit for conductivity cell

A, one of the two platinum electrodes; B, protective mantle of borosilicate glass or silica; c, electric connexions

the resistance of a cube (of the solution) of 1 cm. side. A suitable arrangement of the platinum electrodes is shown in Fig. 5·1, and this fits neatly into a cell of borosilicate glass or silica. The electrodes (which may be bought in many other designs) must be lightly coated with finely divided platinum so that they have a greyish appearance. This coating needs renewing, as described in the literature,* from time to time (perhaps monthly). As the volume contained between the electrodes varies from cell to cell, the first measurement to be made is the specific resistance of a standard solution of potassium chloride.† This gives the cell-constant of the cell, and all future resistance measurements have to be multiplied by this figure to convert them to specific resistances. If the cell is rigidly made, it should retain the same cell-constant until it is replatinized.

A good thermostat is required for conductimetry because conductivity usually increases by 2% for each degree rise in temperature. A thyratron-regulated thermostat, constant to 0·005°, is recommended for fine work, and the filling liquid should be oil rather than water because of the interaction between the latter and alternating current.

A plentiful supply of conductivity water is required. This may be obtained by distilling distilled water containing alkaline potassium permanganate in an atmosphere free from carbon dioxide, or it can be obtained more simply from an ion-exchange column. A specific conductivity of from 1 to 10×10^{-7} ohm^{-1} cm^{-1} is suitable for work with acids with $pK_a < 6·5$.

The measuring instrument is a Wheatstone bridge of which the two ends are connected to the conductivity cell. In fine work, the connexion is made indirectly to avoid transfer of heat. One arm of the bridge can be loaded with standard resistances, usually from a six decade box measuring up to 111,111 ohms. An alternating current, often 1000 cycles per second, is introduced by a thermionic valve oscillator and the balance point of the bridge is detected by a telephone or, preferably, a miniature cathode ray tube. Efficient earthing of the bridge is essential. A small variable condenser is included in the circuit to sharpen the readings. Detailed descriptions of various forms of this bridge network are readily available.‡ One of the most popular designs is that of Jones and

* REILLY and RAE, *Physico-chemical Methods*, 5th ed. 1954, London: Methuen, Vol. 2, pp. 588–636.
† JONES and PRENDERGAST, *J. Amer. Chem. Soc.*, 1937, **59**, 731.
‡ REILLY and RAE, loc. cit.

Josephs.* A two-stage valve amplifier is suitably used in conjunction with such a network.†

Various compact commercial sets are available which incorporate the Wheatstone bridge circuit, valve oscillator, amplifying circuit, decade resistance box and cathode tube indicator. Of these, we instance the Phillips Conductivity Measuring Bridge PR 9500, on the dial of which the resistance can be directly read and has only to be multiplied by the cell-constant to give the specific resistance. This arrangement eliminates the need to solve equation (5.3),

$$R_{solution} = R_{decade-box}\frac{x}{100 - x} \tag{5.3}$$

where the slide-contact divides the bridge-wire, at the point of balance, in the ratio $x/100 - x$. Obach's tables for values of $x/100 - x$ will be found in most handbooks, and in textbooks of practical physical chemistry.‡

Methods

The conductimetric determination of ionization constants has been long practised, and good general descriptions may be found in most works of practical physical chemistry and electrochemistry.‡ After the cell-constant has been measured (see p. 97), a decision must be taken whether to work in molarities (g./litre) or in molalities (g./kilogram), both of which are about equally favoured in the literature. The attractiveness of the latter system is that weighing is independent of temperature effects, so that the bulk of the solution (and in conductivity work there is usually a great bulk of solution) does not have to be kept in the thermostat.

Any volume of solution may be used provided that the electrodes are covered to a depth of at least 1 cm. If the unknown acid is plentiful, each dilution may be made up, independently of the

* JONES and JOSEPHS, *J. Amer. Chem. Soc.*, 1928, **50**, 1049.
† JONES and BOLLINGER, *J. Amer. Chem. Soc.*, 1929, **51**, 2407; DIPPY and HUGHES, *J. Chem. Soc.*, 1928, **50**, 1049.
‡ e.g. FINDLAY, *Practical Physical Chemistry*, 8th ed., 1954. London: Longmans.

others, from separate weighings. Alternatively a stock solution may be made and used to fortify an initially weak solution, which thus becomes stronger progressively. The latter method should be attempted only if it is known that the electrodes are only lightly platinized (the adsorptive powers of heavily platinized electrodes can greatly reduce the concentration of a dilute solution). Finally, one can begin with a concentrated solution from which a given quantity is removed after each measurement and replaced by the same quantity of water. This sequential dilution technique, if carried too far, tends to produce cumulative errors. If the quantity is withdrawn by pipette, a new marking will be required on the stem of the pipette to indicate a 'withdrawal' instead of a 'delivery' volume.

The procedure for obtaining an ionization constant is to place a solution of the unknown substance in the conductivity cell (p. 96), and measure the specific resistance (p. 97) in ohms cm., at the required temperature. The specific resistance, when converted to its reciprocal, becomes the specific conductivity in ohms^{-1} cm^{-1}, and is denoted by the symbol L (the Greek letter kappa as formerly used, caused confusion with K, the symbol for the ionization constant). The solution in the cell is then made stronger or weaker as described above, and equilibrated for temperature. The new specific resistance is measured, and each value of the specific conductivity (L) is converted to the *equivalent conductance* (Λ_c), thus

$$\Lambda_c = 1000L/c \qquad (5.4)$$

where c is the concentration in moles per litre, or per kilogram, as the case may be. The equivalent conductance is suitably tabulated alongside the concentration to which it refers, as in Table 5.1.

Before any calculations can be made, values of Λ_0, the *limiting conductance*, must be obtained by a fresh series of experiments on the corresponding salt (they cannot be accurately derived from the unknown substance itself). To this end, one equivalent of the unknown acid is dissolved in 0·98 equivalent of 0·01N-sodium hydroxide (carbonate-free). The small excess of acid makes little difference to the conductivity whereas a small excess of hydroxyl ions arising

99

by hydrolysis would make a big difference (see Table 5.2). The specific resistance of this solution is measured at a range of dilutions, and the reciprocal of this value is converted to values of Λ by equation (5.4). Each value of Λ is then plotted as $1/\Lambda$ against $\sqrt{c}$ and Λ_0 is obtained by extrapolation.* From the value of $\Lambda_{0\ \text{salt}}$, the $\Lambda_{0\ \text{acid}}$ is obtained by subtracting the limiting conductance of the sodium ion and adding that of the hydrogen ion. Table (5.2) supplies these values.

Returning to the Λ_c values obtained directly on the acid, the conductance ratios Λ_c/Λ_0 can now be worked out and added to the

TABLE 5.1

Determination of the ionization constant of an acid by conductimetry

Substance: Acetic acid $(C_2H_4O_2 = 60 \cdot 05)$.* $\Lambda_0 = 390 \cdot 7$.
  Temperature: $25°$.

a. Without corrections

1	2	3	4
Conc. (moles/litre)	Λ_c	Λ_c/Λ_0	pK_a^c (from equations (5.1) and (5.2))
0·05230	7·20	0·01843	4·743
0·02000	11·56	0·02961	4·743
0·009842	16·37	0·04189	4·744
0·005912	20·96	0·05364	4·745
0·002414	32·21	0·08247	4·747
0·001028	48·13	0·1232·	4·750
0·0002184	96·47	0·2470	4·752
0·0001114	127·71	0·3270	4·753
0·00002801	210·32	0·5384	4·754

Result: Concentration $pK_a = 4 \cdot 75 \pm 0 \cdot 01$ at $25°$, at $I = 9 \times 10^{-4}$ to 2×10^{-5}, and concentration 5×10^{-2} to 3×10^{-5}.

* From MacINNES and SHEDLOVSKY, loc. cit.

* SHEDLOVSKY, *J. Franklin Institute*, 1938, **225**, 739.

(TABLE 5.1), *b*. With corrections

5	6	7	8
Λ_c (repeated from column 2)	α (corrected for mobility by equation (5.9))	pK_a (from column 6 by equation (5.2))	pK_a^T (from column 7, corrected for activity by equation (5.13))
7·20	0·01865	4·732	4·764
11·56	0·02987	4·735	4·760
16·37	0·04222	4·737	4·758
20·96	0·05401	4·739	4·757
32·21	0·08290	4·743	4·757
48·13	0·1238	4·745	4·757
96·47	0·2477	4·749	4·757
127·71	0·3277	4·750	4·756
210·32	0·5393	4·753	4·756

Result: Mobility – corrected pK_a $=4\cdot74 \pm 0\cdot01$ *Result:* Thermo-dynamic pK_a $= 4\cdot76 \pm 0$

TABLE 5.2

Limiting equivalent conductance (Λ_0) of ions in water at various temperatures (in ohms^{-1} cm^2)*

	0°	18°	25°	35°	100°
H^+	225	315	350	397	630
OH^-	105	171	199	—	450
Na^+	27	43	50	62	145
K^+	41	64	74	88	195
Li^+	—	—	39	—	—
NH_4^+	40	64	74	—	180
NEt_4^+	16	28	33	—	—
Cl^-	41	66	76	92	212
NO_3^-	40	62	71	—	195
ClO_4^-	37	59	67	—	185
Acetate	20	35	41	—	—

* These values are from various sources but agree with the values for K^+, Na^+, Li^+, H^+, Cl^- and NO_3^- at 25° of MacINNES, SHEDLOVSKY and LONGSWORTH (*J. Amer. Chem. Soc.*, 1932, **54**, 2758).

Table (as in Table 5·1). If this conductance ratio is taken as identical with α (the fraction ionized) from equation (5.1), the ionization constant (K) can be calculated from equation (5.2). The various values in a set have only to be averaged to give the required answer. This, however, is only the concentration (or 'classical') ionization constant, and the question of applying mobility and activity corrections remains to be discussed in the next section.

In conductimetric work, a set usually consists of from 9 to 12 values. In early studies, these values were usually obtained by a long sequence of twofold dilutions. It is equally permissible to work with only four dilutions, repeating the measurements twice more on freshly prepared solutions. The dilutions may be closer than twofold, or more widely spaced.

Refinements of calculation

Table (5.1) shows, in column 4, a series of values (for the pK_a of acetic acid) which are in excellent agreement. These were obtained with a maximal ionic strength* of 0·0009. But even 0·23M-acetic acid is only 0·9% ionized, and hence the ionic strength is only 0·002. Thus it is evident that concentrations of acid which would create a high ionic strength (I) in a potentiometric titration, give fairly low ionic strengths in conductimetric work unless the acid is a very strong one. For such substances, activity corrections make little difference to the result. The intense study of activity effects by workers in conductimetry arose from their desire to extend the method (*a*) to stronger acids and (*b*) to conductimetric titrations, both of which involve high ionic strengths; they were also pursuing activity effects to discover the nature of interionic forces.

Debye and Hückel† derived, from theoretical reasoning, the expression:

$$\log K_a^T = \log K_a^C - 2A\sqrt{\alpha c} \qquad (5.5)$$

where K_a^T is the thermodynamic ionization constant, i.e. one that

* Ionic strength is defined on p. 58.
† DEBYE and HÜCKEL, *Physikal. Z.*, 1923, **24**, 185, 305, 334.

does not vary with the concentration, K_a^C is the concentration-dependent constant as determined by equation (5.2), A is a constant for the solvent at a given temperature, α is the fraction ionized, and c the concentration. This has already been partly discussed on p. 57.

For water at 25°, A is 0·509, so that for uni-univalent electrolytes, where I is c,

$$\log K_a^T = \log K_a^C - 1 \cdot 018 \sqrt{\alpha c} \tag{5.6}$$

This correction has been much used for refining results and low ionic strengths, but it does not smooth results above I = 0·01 as much as was hoped.

A little later, Onsager* made a different approach to the topic by postulating two sources of interionic attractions in conductimetry, both of them frictional. He considered that the first of these (A) is caused by the applied E.M.F. moving the negatively charged ionic atmosphere in the opposite direction to that in which each positive ion is moving, and hence there is a slight tendency in concentrated solutions for the hydrogen ion to be dragged back with its atmosphere. The second and smaller attraction (B) arises from the electrostatic attraction, between oppositely charged ions, slowing the hydrogen ion in its normal tendency to move in response to the applied E.M.F. Onsager therefore wrote:

$$\Lambda_T = \Lambda_0 - (A + B\Lambda_0)\sqrt{c} \tag{5·7}$$

In water at 25°, equation (5.7) becomes:

$$\Lambda_T = \Lambda_0 - (60 \cdot 2 + 0 \cdot 229\Lambda_0)\sqrt{c} \tag{5.8}$$

(It should be noted that Onsager's A is different from Debye and Hückel's A.)

The next advance was made by MacInnes and Shedlovsky,† who applied both an Onsager-type dynamic correction for varying ionic mobility and a Debye–Hückel-type static correction for residual interionic effects.

These authors introduced the concept of Λ_e to replace Λ_0. This *equivalent ionic conductance* (Λ_e) is the equivalent conductance of

* ONSAGER, *Physikal. Z.*, 1926, **27**, 388; 1927, **28**, 277. † loc. cit.

the totally ionized acid, not at infinite dilution but at the concentration at which the partly ionized acid is being measured. This use of Λ_ε (which is concentration-variable) in place of Λ_0 (which is independent of concentration) was intended to compensate for the steady decrease in ionic mobility with increasing concentration. Thus equation (5.1) becomes:

$$\alpha = \Lambda_c/\Lambda_\varepsilon \qquad (5.9)$$

Values of Λ_ε can obviously be obtained as follows:

$$\Lambda_{\varepsilon \text{ acid}} = \Lambda_{c \text{ HCl}} - \Lambda_{c \text{ NaCl}} + \Lambda_{c \text{ salt of acid}} \qquad (5.10)$$

whence

$$\Lambda_\varepsilon = 390 \cdot 59 - 148 \cdot 61\sqrt{\alpha c} + 165 \cdot 5\,\alpha c(1 - 0 \cdot 2274\sqrt{\alpha c}) \quad (5.11)$$

which is obtained from a series of such equations as:

$$\Lambda_{c \text{ NaCl}} = 126 \cdot 42 - 88 \cdot 53\sqrt{c} + 89 \cdot 5c(1 - 0 \cdot 2274\sqrt{c})^* \quad (5.12)$$

To find each value of Λ_ε involves a series of approximations, the first of which is made by inserting the limiting value of Λ_ε, namely $\Lambda_{0 \text{ acid}}$ into equation (5.1). This value of α is inserted into equation (5.11). A new value of α is thus found and this, in turn, leads to new value of Λ_ε, and so on until repetition does not change the result. Usually three rounds of approximations suffice.

The values of α obtained in this way are shown in column 6 of Table 5.1, and from them values of pK_a (shown in column 7) are derived by equation (5.2). It can be seen that the values in column 7 are less precise than those, so much more simply obtained, in column 4. However, the authors considered the values of column 7 to be more accurate, and they attributed the greater precision of column 4 to a partial cancelling of two opposite errors.

These mobility-corrected ionization constants were at once submitted by MacInnes and Shedlovsky to a Debye–Hückel type correction:

$$\log K_a^T = \log K_a^C - 1 \cdot 013\sqrt{\alpha c} \qquad (5.13)$$

which is a minor variant of equation (5.6), differing principally in that the α of (5.13) is already corrected for mobility. The final

---

* SHEDLOVSKY, *J. Amer. Chem. Soc.*, 1932, **54**, 1411.

values obtained from these calculations, shown in column 8 of Table 5.1, are seen to have become highly smoothed, and give a pK_a for acetic acid of 4.76 ± 0.

This two-stage method of MacInnes and Shedlovsky has been widely used and is considered to be highly accurate for activity corrections up to $I = 0.02$. A more complex formula, based on similar principles but requiring many successive approximations, was put forward by Fuoss and Kraus.* This has proved suitable for concentrations up to 0.1M, and pK values (for acids) as low as -1. A slight simplification of this formula is available.† It may seem, from the example of Table 5.1, that activity corrections are unnecessary to attain the degree of precision required for routine determination of pK_a values, say, ± 0.06. However, activity correction is essential (i) for weaker acids which must be measured either in very concentrated solutions, or in the presence of much sodium hydroxide (see p. 95), and (ii) for strong acids and bases, because they produce a high ionic strength.

* FUOSS and KRAUS, *J. Amer. Chem. Soc.*, 1933, **55**, 476.
† SHEDLOVSKY, *J. Franklin Institute*, 1938, **225**, 739.

6

Solubility–Ionization Relationships

Ionization constants in preparative work

In the preparative laboratory, maximal yields can be obtained by utilizing the ionization constant of the substance being made. When, as is so often the case, the medium is water and the substance is present as a dissolved salt, the maximal yield is obtained by adjusting the pH to the value that is, numerically, 2 units on the far side of the pK_a. Thus an acidic solution of *p*-toluidine may be at pH 1, but the pK_a is 5·1 and hence the solution should be adjusted to pH 7·1. If the substance is insoluble in water, this rule gives the nearest pH at which the maximal yield of precipitate can be obtained; if the substance is soluble in water, this rule indicates the nearest pH at which an immiscible solvent will extract the desired substance most efficiently. The principle involved is simply that a neutral molecule is less water-soluble than the corresponding ion, and, if the neutral molecule is too water-soluble to precipitate, it is more easily shaken out of solution than an ion. Reference to Appendix IV shows that when the pH is made equal to the pK_a, the substance is still 50% ionized, but when the pK has been exceeded by 1 unit of pH, the substance is about 10% ionized, and when it has been exceeded by 2 units, it is only 1% ionized.

To stabilize the preparation at the chosen pH, it is desirable to effect the liberation with a reagent (a common acid or base) which has a pK_a near to this pH, because all reagents have the best buffering capacity at a pH equal to their pK_a. Sulphuric acetic and phosphoric acids (with pK values of about 2, 5 and 7 respectively) are much used as liberators on the acid side of neutrality, and they are usefully supplemented by citric acid which has three close pK values (3·1, 4·7, and 6·4). Substances useful for the alkaline range will be found in Table 4·1. When liberation is begun by reagents which have pK values between 4 and 10, it is more economically completed by hydrochloric acid or sodium hydroxide; this is because the first-named reagents change the pH very little after a certain amount has been added, but act as excellent buffers at the chosen pH. Hence alternatively, a *salt* of the desired reagent may be used in place of the free reagent, in which case hydrochloric acid or sodium hydroxide is then added until the desired pH is obtained.

If the pH of the preparation is not stabilized in this way, the pH will change during precipitation in such a way that ionization is increased and the yield falls.

Amphoteric substances are best adjusted to a pH that is half-way between the acidic and the basic pK_a values, or else to a pH that lies between the two pK_a values and is at least two units away from any pK_a value.

When preparing a new substance, it is worthwhile obtaining a sample of it, no matter how wastefully, from a small preliminary run so that the pK_a can be determined very early in the work. With this information much better yields can be obtained from the following batches.

The principal difficulties that may be encountered on applying this method arise from the fact that many preparations are made in highly concentrated solutions so that activity effects, and even crystal-lattice effects, supervene. In spite of this, the method has so much to offer that it should be put into operation on every possible occasion. (For examples, see footnote.*)

Another useful application of the method can be made in purifying a base that contains a small proportion of a weaker base. The material is dissolved in acid and adjusted to the lowest pH at which all the impurity is non-ionized, as calculated from Appendix IV. The impurity can then usually be filtered off or extracted with a solvent. By this 'pre-precipitation technique', many a base can

---

* ALBERT, *J. Chem. Soc.*, 1955, 2690.

be obtained pure with less loss of material than occurs in re-crystallization. Acids, including phenols, can be similarly purified in alkaline solution.

Prediction of solubility from ionization constants

The solubility of an acid in an alkaline solution depends on two properties: the ionization constant, and the intrinsic solubility of the neutral molecule. Thus heptanoic acid readily dissolves in a buffer solution of pH 7 whereas its higher homologue stearic acid is practically insoluble, although both acids have the same pK_a. The low intrinsic solubility of stearic acid provides the explanation.

The observed solubility (S_o' of an acid at a given pH is due to two terms, the solubility of the neutral molecule (a saturated solution) and the solubility of the anion (far from saturated). Thus:

$$S_o' = [HA] + [A^-] \qquad (6.1)$$

but

$$[A^-] = \frac{K_a[HA]}{[H^+]} \quad \text{from} \quad (1.3)$$

hence

$$S_o' = [HA] + \frac{K_a[HA]}{[H^+]}$$

$$= [HA](1 + \text{antilog}\,(pH - pK_a)) \qquad (6.2)$$

To express S_o' at, say, pH 4·32 we write $S_o^{4·32}$.

In equation (6.2), [HA] equals the intrinsic solubility, i.e. the molar concentration of a saturated solution in which ionization has been prevented. Thus we may write:

$$S_o' = S_i(1 + \text{antilog}\,(pH - pK_a)) \qquad (6.3)$$

The intrinsic solubility (S_i) of an acid is usually determined in 0·01N-hydrochloric acid, and that of a base in 0·01N-sodium hydroxide. Often the figures for S_i differ only slightly from those observed for S_o' in water, because the term $(1 + \text{antilog}\,(pH - pK_a))$ in equation (6.3) is negligible for those weak acids and bases that are only moderately soluble. The usefulness of equation (6.3) for acids becomes apparent in more alkaline solutions, and some examples are given in Table 6.1.

TABLE 6.1

Solubility of acids at various pH values (20°)

Solubility (moles/litre)*	Lauric acid $C_{12}H_{24}O_2 = 200$ $(pK_a = 4.95)$	Heptanoic acid $C_7H_{14}O_2 = 130$ $(pK_a = 4.90)$	Benzoic acid $C_7H_6O_2 = 122$ $(pK_a = 4.12)$
S_i	8.5×10^{-6}	2.2×10^{-2}	2.3×10^{-2}
S_o^3	8.5×10^{-6}	2.2×10^{-2}	2.5×10^{-2}
S_o^4	9.1×10^{-6}	2.4×10^{-2}	4.0×10^{-2}
S_o^5	2.0×10^{-5}	5.1×10^{-2}	2.0×10^{-1}
S_o^6	1.1×10^{-4}	3.1×10^{-1}	1.8
S_o^7	1.1×10^{-3}	1.7	(18.3)

* S_i means intrinsic solubility of the neutral molecule; S_o^3 means observed solubility at pH 3, and so forth.

It is seen from Table 6.1 that although two homologues of acetic acid (namely lauric acid and heptanoic acid) have almost the same pK_a, they have very different intrinsic solubilities. When the pH is increased to equal the pK_a numerically, the solubilities are only doubled (these are the S_o^5 values). However, when the pH is increased to 2 units above the pK_a, the solubility of heptanoic acid is quite large (1.7M, or about 1 part in 5), whereas that of lauric acid is much less (0.001M, or 1 part in 5000). Benzoic acid, which has about the same intrinsic solubility as heptanoic acid, but is a stronger acid, shows the expected increased solubility over heptanoic acid. Expressed in another way, the effect of bringing lauric acid to a pH that is 2 units more alkaline than the pK_a has been to ionize 99% of it; however, as the intrinsic solubility is so low, the dissolution of 99% as anion still leaves the solution completely saturated at 0.001M (total species) and no more can be dissolved at this pH.

In using equation (6.3), too much reliance must not be placed on values in excess of 0.1M because of activity effects. It must be remembered also that, whereas an ion may be supposed to have infinite solubility, the salt that it forms with the gegenion (e.g. with Na^+) has a finite solubility which depends on the lattice energy of the solid state.

Conversely it may be required to know what intrinsic solubility a substance must possess to achieve a given concentration in, say, N-sodium hydroxide. For this purpose, equation (6.3) is rearranged to:

$$S_i = S_o^{14}/1 + \text{antilog} (14 - pK_a) \qquad (6.4)$$

If S_o^{14}, the required concentration at pH 14, is $0.1M$, then:

> for an acid of pK_a 5, S_i is $10^{-10}M$
> for an acid of pK_a 8, S_i is $10^{-7}M$
> for an acid of pK_a 11, S_i is $10^{-4}M$

On referring to Table 6.1, it becomes evident that even lauric acid can give a $0.1M$ solution in sodium hydroxide, although it barely reaches this concentration at pH 9 (S_o^9 for lauric acid is $0.09M$, from equation (6.3)).

For bases, the equation equivalent to (6.3) is,

$$S_o' = S_i(1 + \text{antilog} (pK_a - pH)) \qquad (6.5)$$

Determination of ionization constants from solubilities

The solubility method for determining pK_a is rather laborious but proves useful in those rare cases where (*a*) the substance is too insoluble in water for the potentiometric or conductimetric methods, and (*b*) the molecular and ionic ultraviolet spectra are either too similar or totally lacking. If the spectra are identical, this forms no barrier to their use for analysing the saturated solutions, which otherwise are examined by gravimetry (after precipitation with a reagent) or colorimetry (after addition of a colour-forming reagent).

The solubility method* is applied in this way. First, the solubility (S_i) of the neutral molecular species is determined at a pH where it is suspected that this species will predominate. Next, two further determinations are made, 0.5 pH unit above and below that formerly used, in order to see whether the same solubility figure is obtained, a necessary condition to make sure that the original value was the true S_i. These three results should agree to within the experimental error of the analytical technique.

* KREBS and SPEAKMAN, *J. Chem. Soc.*, 1945, 593.

Next, the solubility is redetermined at a pH near to where the pK_a is suspected to be. From this result an approximate value of the pK_a is calculated from a rearrangement of equations (6.3) and (6.5) namely,

$$pK_a = pH - \log((S'_0/S_i) - 1) \text{ for acids} \tag{6.6}$$

and $\qquad pK_a = pH + \log((S'_0/S_i) - 1) \text{ for bases} \tag{6.7}$

A set of seven pK_a values is then obtained by determining solubilities at a series of pH values, preferably distributed evenly within the range $pK_a \pm 1$. The values are averaged, as on p. 13, to give the result.

Because solubilities are highly sensitive to the presence of foreign ions, it is necessary to carry out the determinations at a constant ionic strength (defined on p. 58). For the pH range 3 to 11, the buffers in Table 4.1 are suitable if used at 0·005M strength in 0·1M-sodium chloride.

TABLE 6.2

Determination of an acidic ionization constant by the solubility method*

Substance: Sulphadiazine. $C_{10}H_{10}N_4O_2S$ = 250·3. *Temperature:* 25°.
S_i = 6·16 mg. per 100 ml., at pH 4·3.
$\quad$ = $2·464 \times 10^{-4}$M.

1	2	3	4	5
pH	S'_0 (mg./100 ml.)	$(S'_0/S_i) - 1$	log column 3	pK_a (= pH − column 4)
6·01	8·5	0·38	−0·42	6·43
6·35	11·1	0·80	−0·10	6·45
6·82	19·4	2·15	0·33	6·49
7·23	43·5	6·06	0·78	6·45
7·56	86·0	13·00	1·11	6·45

Result: pK_a = 6·45 ± 0·04 at I = 0·1, and 20°, using all five values from the rather small set.

* Example from KREBS and SPEAKMAN (loc. cit.).

111

In practice, an excess of the unknown is shaken in a thermo-static bath with these buffer solutions under an inert atmosphere, until a steady concentration of the unknown is found on analysis. The undissolved solid is then separated by centrifugation and the pH is measured at once. Three hours' shaking sufficed for the example reported in Table 6.2.

For amphoteric substances, S_i is conveniently found by plotting S_0' against $1/\{H^+\}$ and extrapolating the straight line to $1/\{H^+\} = 0$.

No hydrogen- or hydroxyl-ion corrections are needed in this method because no stoicheiometric concentrations are used. Because of the swamping ionic strength at which these determinations must be done, the results differ considerably from thermodynamic constants. The method is not accurate in highly alkaline solutions if there is uncertainty about the pH (see p. 19).

Related methods

pK_a values may similarly be determined by partition methods with immiscible solvents,* also by the use of ion-exchange columns. A preparative method has been described for separating two weak acids of similar pK_a values by countercurrent distribution between an organic solvent and an aqueous phase containing their salts.† The process uses a Craig 20 tube system modified to permit solvent flow in either direction. Fifteen double transfers served to separate *o*- and *p*-toluic acids whose pK_a values differ by only 0·47.

* FARMER and WARTH, *J. Chem. Soc.*, 1904, **85**, 1713.
† BARKER and BEECHAM, *Australian J. Chem.*, 1960, **13**, 1.

7

Zwitterions (Dipolar Ions)

Küster coined the word 'zwitterion' in 1897 to describe the nature of certain indicators, such as methyl orange, which act as though they have one fully ionized acidic group and one fully ionized basic group in each molecule. The names 'amphions' and 'dipolar ions' have also been put forward to describe these internal salts. But there are many amphoteric substances which are not zwitterions. Thus, a substance may have both an acidic and a basic group, but these cannot form an internal salt unless both groups are simultaneously ionized and this depends on the magnitudes of their pK_a values.

$$H_2N-\text{(ring)}-OH \qquad \overset{+}{H_3}N.CH_2.CO_2H \xleftarrow{H^+} \overset{+}{H_3}N.CH_2.CO_2^- \xleftarrow{H^+} H_2N.CH_2.CO_2^-$$

(I)　　　　　　　(II)　　　　　　(III)　　　　　　(IV)

Zwitterions and ordinary amphoteric substances compared

We will discuss m-aminophenol (I) as an example of an ordinary amphoteric substance, and glycine (aminoacetic acid) (III) as an example of a zwitterion.

m-Aminophenol has two pK_a values, 4·2 and 9·9; and these are similar to those of two related substances, aniline (4·6) and phenol (10·0). If the values for m-aminophenol are used in conjunction with Appendix IV (p. 173), the following sequence of ionizations can be worked out. At, and below, pH 2·2, the basic group is completely ionized and the acidic group is not ionized; at pH 4·2 the basic group is only half ionized (all figures are averages for a large number of similar molecules considered together). Between

113

pH 6·2 and 7·9, neither group is ionized, but at pH 9·9 the acidic group is half ionized. At, and above, pH 11·9, the acidic group is entirely ionized, and the basic group not ionized. Such substances present few problems: their pK_a values may readily be determined (as on p. 56) and assigned to the relevant ionizing groups.

Zwitterions present a different pattern of ionization. In highly acidic solutions only cations are present, e.g. (II) for glycine, and in highly alkaline solutions only anions, e.g. (IV). Thus far, the resemblance to ordinary amphoteric substances is complete. The difference occurs at intermediate pH values, where the majority of molecules have *both* groups ionized. Because of the doubly charged nature of a zwitterion, it can prove confusing to speak of anion formation with alkali; and of cation formation with acids. It is better to speak of the change from (III) to (II) as 'proton gained', and from (III) to (IV) as 'proton lost'.

Every molecule which has an acidic pK_a numerically lower than the basic pK_a is a zwitterion, in so far as it has acidic and basic groups strong enough to neutralize one another.*

Unlike the example of *m*-aminophenol, discussed above, zwitterions often have pK_a values which differ considerably from those of simpler analogues (this happens only when the acidic and basic group are near together, or are separated mainly by a conjugated chain of double bonds). The ionization of the basic group creates a positive charge which attracts electrons and hence strengthens a nearby acidic group so that the pK_a of the latter falls. Conversely, the ionization of the acidic group creates a negative charge which releases electrons and thus makes a contribution towards strengthening the basic group (this effect would be partly neutralized by the electron-attracting (base-weakening) effect of any doubly bound oxygen atom present in the acidic group). In ordinary amphoteric substances the mutual interaction of the groups is much slighter because only one kind of group can be ionized at a time.

The pK_a values of amphoteric substances are most readily determined by potentiometry. The spectrometric method, although

* BJERRUM, N., *Z. Physik. Chem.*, 1923, **104**, 147.

more time-consuming, also gives good results. The values found are, by convention, called pK_a^1, pK_a^2, pK_a^3, etc., in order of increasing pK_a. This convention is necessary, as it is not always possible to assign the pK_a values to a given group without much further work. If tests (see below) show that the substance is not a zwitterion, then no further work is needed, for the pK_a found during titration with acid will be that of a basic group, and the pK_a found during titration with alkali will be that of the acidic group. But when a zwitterion is titrated with acid, a proton is added to the carboxylic anion, e.g. (III) gives (II), which is quite the reverse of what happens with an ordinary amphoteric substance.

Hence the pK_a values of a new natural product may be recorded e.g. as 'pK_a (proton gained) 3·3, pK_a (protons lost) 7·4 and 9·3', and the results may remain in this state for some time until each pK_a can be assigned to its ionizing group. Thus the above figure of 3·3, obtained by titration with acid, would be that of a weak base if the substance were an ordinary amphoteric substance, but it would be that of a strong acid if the substance were a zwitterion.

Tests for zwitterions

A substance is often suspected to be a zwitterion if it is more soluble in water, less soluble in organic solvents, and has a higher melting point, than related substances with only one ionizing group. These are all signs of a salt-like character, but are insufficient as evidence of zwitterion character because they are found in many non-electrolytes of fairly high dipole moment (say 6 Debye units).

Measurements of dielectric constants are more discriminating. The dielectric constant of a solution is given by:

$$D = D_0 + \delta C \qquad (7.1)$$

where D_0 is the dielectric constant of the solvent, δ is the dielectric increment, and C is the concentration. The dielectric increment for zwitterions is a large positive number which indicates that each molecule has a large dipole moment. A zwitterion should have a dipole moment of at least 15 Debye units, as compared with a maximum of 6·5 units for a highly dipolar (but non-ionized) molecule such as *p*-nitroaniline. This test is not often used, because the apparatus is not widely available. In its place, ordinary dipole moments can seldom be measured because of the feeble solubility of zwitterions in solvents of low dielectric constant.

Another sensitive test for zwitterions, the measurement of electrostriction from the apparent molal volume, also requires apparatus which is not widely available.

Of the easily applied tests for zwitterions, the following are the best:

(*a*) If at least one of the pK_a values is markedly different from that of a singly charged analogue such as an ester or an O-ether, the substance is a zwitterion (see below, p. 117, for an example).

(*b*) If the pK_a, found by titration with acid, rises or is stationary instead of falling when the titration is repeated in 50–70% ethanol, the substance is a zwitterion* (see below, p. 117, for an example).

However (*a*) and (*b*) could be negative, and the substance may nevertheless be a zwitterion.

(*c*) If the substance absorbs in the ultraviolet and one group is a carboxylic acid (the spectrum of which should not change appreciably on ionization), and the other group is an aromatic amino-group, then a large shift, in the long-wave band of the spectrum, to shorter wave-lengths on adding alkali indicates that the substance is a zwitterion. This rule, slightly modified, has been used to demonstrate the zwitterionic character of the pyridine carboxylic acids.†

In explanation of test (*b*), it may be recalled that alcohol, by depressing the ionization of both acids and bases, makes the pK_a of an acid higher and that of a base lower.

In many zwitterions, the 'proton lost' pK_a (as revealed by titration with alkali) reacts abnormally to alcohol by not showing the expected depression. This has been attributed to the unusual nature of the equilibrium: $HZ^{+-} \rightleftharpoons H^+ + Z^-$ in which all parti-

* JUKES and SCHMIDT, *J. Biol. Chem.*, 1934, **105**, 359.
† GREEN and TONG, *J. Amer. Chem. Soc.*, 1956, **78**, 4896.

cipants are charged, and the number of charges remains constant. However, amino-derivatives of sulphonic acids usually react normally to alcohol.

Glycine (III), when titrated in water at 20°, shows two pK_a values, one at 2·2 (proton gained) and one at 9·9 (proton lost). The corresponding methyl ester has only one pK_a (7·7), which corresponds to the ionization of its amino-group. On numerical grounds, the value 7·7, from the ester, is more related to 9·9 than to 2·2 in glycine. Hence the value 9·9 must refer to the ionization of the amino-group of glycine, because 7·7 refers to the ionization of the amino-group in the ester. This is true, even though the 7·7 value was obtained by titrating the ester with acid, and the 9·9 value by titrating glycine with alkali (a mental barrier which sometimes arises here may be overcome by picturing the ester, supplied as the hydrochloride, being titrated with alkali). The interpretation, that the 9·9 value refers to the equilibrium (III) $\rightleftharpoons$ (IV), is confirmed by re-titration in 50% ethanol, when *both* pK_a values increase (to 2·7 and 10·0 respectively) which indicates that the substance is a zwitterion (see p. 116), and hence that the upper pK_a belongs to the ionization of the basic group.

The following factors govern the magnitude of the pK_a values of glycine. The pK_a of acetic acid is 4·8, but the ionized amino-group in the glycine zwitterion is electron-attracting, and hence acid-strengthening, and the anionic group is near enough to be strengthened by this to 2·2. The methyl ester of glycine, thanks to the inductive $(-I)$ effect of the $-CO_2CH_3$ group, is 1000 times weaker a base than methylamine (the pK_a of the ester is 7·7 compared to 10·7 for methylamine). This inductive effect should be the same in the neutral molecule of glycine (V), a substance which exists in minute amount in equilibrium with the zwitterion of glycine (III), as we shall discuss later. That the inductive effect would be the same in (V) as in its methyl ester follows from the fact that acids and their esters have the same dipole moments. That the pK_a of glycine is 9·9 instead of 7·7 is thus further proof of its zwitterion nature. The magnitude of the value 9·9 is the resultant of two opposing tendencies, (*a*) the base-weakening inductive effect of the carboxyl-group, and (b) the strengthening effect of an anion (through electron release) on a basic-group near enough to be influenced. Hence glycine is only 6 times (0·8 pK unit) weaker than methylamine.

$$H_2N.CH_2.CO_2H \qquad H_3\overset{+}{N}.CH_2CH_2CH_2CH_2.CO_2^{-}$$

(V)   (VI)   (VII)

The effect of removing the two charged groups from one another's influence is seen in δ-aminovaleric acid (VI) which has pK_a values of 4·3 and 10·8 which are very near to those of acetic acid (4·8) and methylamine (10·7) respectively (the pK_a of the methyl ester is 10·15).

Calculations

Useful exercise in calculations can be had by considering the pK_a values of glycine (2·2 and 9·9) in conjunction with Appendix IV. Thus, at pH 1·2 only 10% of the acidic groups, but all of the basic groups, are ionized. Hence, at this pH, 10% of the substance is present as zwitterions and 90% as cations. These calculations can be repeated at any other pH values. It will be found that glycine is almost entirely zwitterionic between pH 3·3 and 8·9 (i.e. 1 unit above the lower pK_a and 1 unit below the upper pK_a). Above 10·9, glycine is largely anionic.

Similar calculations with an ordinary amphoteric substance, p-aminobenzoic acid (basic pK_a 2·7, acidic pK_a 4·8) show that, at pH 1·7, 90% of the basic and none of the acidic groups are ionized and hence 90% of the substance is present as cations. At pH 3·8, solutions of p-aminobenzoic acid contain roughly 91% of neutral molecules, 7·4% of zwitterions, 1·6% of anions, and an inappreciable percentage of cations. This may be verified from Appendix IV.*

Activity corrections

For purposes of activity corrections, zwitterions are assumed to

* The calculations are : 2·7 − 3·8 = −1·1 (7·4% cation); 4·8 − 3·8 = +1·0 (9·0% anion). 9·0 − 7·4 = 1·6% excess anion +7·4% zwitterion.

have zero ionic strength. However, in the course of a titration they are converted to cations or anions to which the usual equations apply. When zwitterions are used as buffers, they are usually accorded the ionic strength of uni-univalent electrolytes.

Tautomeric ratios

Any zwitterion is in tautomeric equilibrium with the correspond-ing neutral molecule; e.g. (III) is in equilibrium with a minute amount of (V). Ebert* showed that the ratio (R) could be calculated by assuming that the basic pK_a of the neutral molecule (V) is almost the same as that of the corresponding ester (for reasons given above). Thus, for glycine the pK_a for the equilibrium (V) ⇌ (II) is taken as 7·7. But the pK_a for the equilibrium (III) ⇌ (II) is 2·2. Ebert derived the equation:

$$R = \text{antilog } (pK_{OMe} - pK_Z) - 1 \qquad (7.2)$$

where pK_{OMe} is the pK_a of the ester, and pK_Z is the lower pK_a of the zwitterion. Thus for glycine, R = 224,000, which is the number of zwitterions for each neutral molecule. The ratio R is in-dependent of pH, but no tautomerism exists in the cation or anion. R is conveniently expressed as log R, which is 5·4 for glycine, 5·9 for δ-aminovaleric acid (VI).

For nicotinic acid (pyridine-3-carboxylic acid), which is con-ventionally written as (VII), the following pK_a values are available: 2·07 (proton added), 4·81 (proton lost), 3·13 (methyl ester, proton added). Formula (7·2) gives:

$$R = \text{antilog } (3·13 - 2·07) - 1$$
$$= 11·48 - 1$$
$$= 10·48$$

Thus there are about 10 molecules of zwitterion for every one of the neutral molecule pictured as (VII). Both zwitterion and neutral molecule are in equilibrium with the cation, but different constants are involved in each case, and the pK_a of 2·07 given

---

* EBERT, *Z. phys. Chem.*, 1926, **121**, 385; EDSALL and BLANCHARD, *J. Amer. Chem. Soc.*, 1933, **55**, 2337.

above is a composite of these. This concept becomes clearer when overlapping constants are considered.

Overlapping constants

When an acidic and a basic group ionize in such a way that the two pK_a values are closer than 2·5 units, the values in a set have to be rectified by the calculations already described for two neighbouring constants (see p. 51). Even when two precise constants are obtained in this way, each of them must be assigned to *both* groups, a peculiarity of zwitterions with overlapping constants.

For example, the amino-acid tyrosine has three pK_a values, the two higher of which overlap ($pK_a^2 = 9·11$; $pK_a^3 = 10·13$) and correspond to a phenolic and an amino-group, but not respectively. For these are both composite constants (called 'macroscopic constants'), which are the resultants of four true constants (called 'microscopic constants'). Both the zwitterion and the neutral molecule give the same anion, but in each case the constants are different; likewise each give the same cation, but again the constants vary. Careful spectrographic work* has shown the four real constants to be:

$$
\begin{array}{ccc}
\mathrm{O^-} & \xleftarrow{\;9·70\;} & \mathrm{O^-} \\[2pt]
\mathrm{^+NH_3} & & \mathrm{NH_2} \\
{\scriptstyle 9·63}\Big\uparrow\Big\downarrow & & \Big\downarrow{\scriptstyle 10·05} \\
\mathrm{OH} & & \mathrm{OH} \\[2pt]
\mathrm{^+NH_3} & \xrightarrow[9·28]{} & \mathrm{NH_2}
\end{array}
$$

Note that no real constant is quite so low, and none quite so high, as the two composite constants.

Cysteine† and 3-hydroxypyridine are further examples of zwitterions with overlapping constants and four simultaneous ionization processes.

* EDSALL, MARTIN and HOLLINGSWORTH, *Proc. Nat. Acad. Sci.*, 1958, **44**, 505.
† GRAFIUS and NEILANDS, *J. Amer. Chem. Soc.*, 1955, **77**, 3389.

8

Ionization Constants of
400 Typical Acids and Bases

A study of the influence of structure on ionization is worthwhile for many reasons. Knowledge of the ionization constants of newly discovered substances can provide good clues to constitution. In synthetic work, prediction of the ionization constant can suggest the best pH for extraction or precipitation. In the preparation of new biologically active substances, the prediction of pK_a in advance of synthesis is useful when the required biological action is known to be limited to substances lying within a certain pK_a range.

The following Tables together with the accompanying text, should provide a satisfactory introduction to the process of correlating ionization constants and structure. The following order has been observed: organic acids precede organic bases, and the organic section precedes the inorganic section. In any organic section, aliphatic substances precede aromatic substances. Heterocyclic substances are placed at the end of the appropriate aliphatic or aromatic tables, according to their heteroparaffinic or heteroaromatic nature.

A. ORGANIC SECTION

I. The oxygen acids (monobasic)

The aliphatic carboxylic acids

A very good introduction to the inductive effects of substituents can be obtained by studying aliphatic carboxylic acids. Two substituents, the methyl-group, and the carboxylic anion, possess a positive inductive effect (+I), and hence are acid-weakening. All other common substituents have a negative inductive effect (−I), and hence are acid-strengthening.

The acid-weakening effect of the methyl-group is seen by comparing acetic and formic acids in Table 8.1 Further increases in chain length have little effect, as can be seen in this Table up to C_8, and, in other work,* up to C_{18}. The series: methylacetic (propionic), dimethylacetic, and trimethylacetic acids reveals that even the substitution of several methyl-groups into acetic acid itself causes little further decrease of acid strength. The carboxylic anion substituent is treated in Section II (Dibasic acids) and Table 8.6.

The many acid-strengthening groups are most conveniently studied as substituents of acetic acid (see Table 8.1), because not many substituted formic acids are available. These −I substituents are conveniently divided into those which reduce the pK_a by 4 units, by 3 units, by 2 units and by 1 unit, as follows:

Substituents lowering pK_a by about 4 units: $-CF_3$, CCl_3; by 3 units: $-CHCl_2$, $-NO_2$, $-C{\equiv}C-$; by 2 units: $-SO_2CH_3$, $-CN$, $-SCN$, $-F$, $-Cl$, $-Br$, $-NH_3^+$; by 1 unit: $-I$, $-CO_2Et$, $-CONH_2$, $COCH_3$, $-SCH_3$, $-OCH_3$, $-OH$.

The acid-strengthening effect of a −I group persists, although to an ever-diminishing extent, when the group is separated from the anion by an ever-increasing number of methylene groups, which are poor conductors of electrons. For example, α-trifluoro-acetic, β-trifluoropropionic and γ-trifluorobutyric acids have pK_a values of 0·23, 3·02 and 4·16 respectively. A less inductive group causes less disturbance, e.g. α-, β- and γ- chlorobutyric acids have pK_a values of 2·84, 4·06 and 4·52 respectively.

The double-bond, and the phenyl-group have a small −I effect, and are also capable of a certain amount of acid-strengthening through a positive tautomeric effect (+T) when their double-bond can conjugate with other bonds. Thus phenylacetic acid is a little stronger than acetic acid, but phenylformic acid (benzoic

* JUKES and SCHMIDT, *J. Biol. Chem.*, 1935, **110**, 9.

acid) is a little weaker than formic acid, and cinnamic acid is a little weaker than acrylic acid. The heightened strength of *cis*- (compared to *trans*-) cinnamic acid has been attributed to the shorter distance separating the phenyl- and carboxylic-groups in the *cis*-isomer, permitting a —I effect across the intervening space.

Any group which has latent tautomeric (T) properties, and there are few which have not, can transmit this through a double-bond (or a chain of conjugated double-bonds) to the carboxylic acid group. Thus, in tetrolic acid, the +T potentialities of the methyl-group are exerted to weaken the acid (see Table 8.1). This effect will be discussed further in the next section (this page).

The alicyclic carboxylic acids are similar in strength to the aliphatic acids, regardless of the ring-size.

The acid-strengthening nature of cationic groups (e.g. $-NH_3^+$) is treated under Section IX, and Table 8.13.

The aromatic carboxylic acids

A selection of aromatic carboxylic acids is given in Table 8.2. Many obvious gaps in the list arise from the poor aqueous solubility of a number of these acids, although this difficulty is not insurmountable.

Each of the three positions of substitution in the benzene ring has marked individuality. The meta position is the most easily understood, because groups placed there exercise an almost pure +I or —I effect, just as in the saturated aliphatic acids. Although these groups retain their sign, the extent of their inductive effect is much less because the distance is greater, and many striking differences seen in the aliphatic series are decreased.

In the para position the I effect should be smaller because of increased distance. However, the para position is (from considerations of valency) capable of facilitating tautomerism and hence almost every substituent placed in this position is capable of exerting a T effect.* If the sign of both I and T effects is the same, the effect is increased. Thus the methyl-group has +I and +T

---

* Perhaps the only common substituents that lack a T effect are ions such as $-SO_3^-$ and $-NH_3^+$.

TABLE 8.1

Aliphatic and alicyclic carboxylic acids (monobasic)

(in water)

Abbreviations for methods: P, potentiometry with a hydrogen or glass electrode; P_Q with a quinhydrone electrode; $P^{0.01}$ (etc.), potentiometry at a concentration of 0·01; T, thermodynamic; C, conductimetry; I, indicator method; K, kinetic measurements on decomposition of an unstable substance.

Acid		pK_a	°C	Method	Ref.
Homologues and isomers					
Formic		3·752	25	PT	A
Acetic		4·756	25	PT	B
		4·756	25	CT	C
Propionic		4·874	25	PT	D
n-Valeric (C_5)		4·860	25	CT	E
n-Octanoic		4·894	25	CT	E
Dimethylacetic (isobutyric)		4·860	25	CT	E
Trimethylacetic (pivalic)		5·050	25	CT	E
Substituted acetic acids	R				
(RCH_2CO_2H)					
Trifluoro-	$-F_3$	0·23	25	CT	F
Trichloro-	$-Cl_3$	0·66	20	I	G
Dichloro-	$-Cl_2$	1·25	18	CT	H
Nitro-	$-NO_2$	1·68	18	K	I
Methylsulphonyl-	$-SO_2CH_3$	2·36	25	C	J
Cyano-	$-CN$	2·47	25	CT	K
Thiocyanato-	$-SCN$	2·58	25	C	L
Fluoro-	$-F$	2·57	20	CT	M
Chloro-	$-Cl$	2·85 / 2·87	20 / 25	CT	M
Bromo-	$-Br$	2·89 / 2·90	20 / 25	CT	M
Iodo-	$-I$	3·16	20	CT	M
Ethoxycarbonyl- (ethyl hydrogen malonate)	$-CO_2Et$	3·35	25	C	N
Carbamoyl- (malonamic acid)	$-CONH_2$	3·64	25	C	O
Acetyl- (acetoacetic acid)[a]	$-COCH_3$	3·58	18	P_Q	P
Methylthio-	$-SCH_3$	3·72	25	C	Q
Methoxy-	$-OCH_3$	3·53	25	C	R
Hydroxyl- (glycolic acid)[b]	$-OH$	3·83	25	PT	S
Phenyl-[c]	$-C_6H_5$	4·31	25	CT	T

Acid	pK$_a$	°C	Method	Ref.
Unsaturated acids (*trans*, except where otherwise marked)				
Acrylic (CH_2:CH.CO_2H)	4·26	25	CT	U
Penta-2-en-l-oic	4·69	25	CT	V
Penta-3-en-l-oic	4·51	25	CT	V
Cinnamic	4·44	25	CT	U
Cinnamic (*cis*)	3·88	25	CT	U
Propiolic (CH:C.CO_2H)	1·84	25	P$^{0.01}$	W
But-2-yn-l-oic (tetrolic acid)	2·60	25	P$^{0.01}$	W
Alicyclic acids				
Cyclopropane carboxylic	4·83	25	P$_Q$	X
Cyclopentane carboxylic	4·99	25	P$_Q$	X
Cyclohexane carboxylic	{4·91	25	P$_Q$	X
	{4·90	25	CT	Y

[a] cf. Acetoformic (pyruvic acid): 2·49.
[b] cf. α-Hydroxypropionic (lactic acid): 3·86.
[c] cf. Phenylformic (benzoic acid): 4·20.

A. HARNED and EMBREE, *J. Amer. Chem. Soc.*, 1934, **56**, 1042; B. HARNED and EHLERS, ibid., 1932, **54**, 1350; C. MacINNES and SHEDLOVSKY, ibid., p. 1429; D. HARNED and EHLERS, ibid., 1933, **55**, 2379; E. DIPPY, *J. Chem. Soc.*, 1938, 1222; F. HENNE and FOX, *J. Amer. Chem. Soc.*, 1951, **73**, 2323; G. HALBAN and BRÜLL, *Helv. chim. Acta*, 1944, **27**, 1719; H. RANDALL and FAILEY, *Chem. Rev.*, 1927, **4**, 291; I. PEDERSEN, *Acta Chem. Scand.*, 1947, **1**, 437; J. MELANDER, *Svensk Kem. Tidskr.*, 1934, **46**, 99 (*Chem. Abs.*, 1934, **28**, 5408); K. FEATES and IVES, *J. Chem. Soc.*, 1956, 2798; L. OSTWALD, *Z. physik. Chem.*, 1889, **3**, 170; M. IVES and PRIOR, *J. Chem. Soc.*, 1955, 2104; N. WALKER, ibid., 1892, **61**, 696; O. JEFFREY and VOGEL, ibid., 1934, 1101; P. PEDERSEN, *J. Phys. Chem.*, 1934, **38**, 993; Q LARSSON, *Ber.*, 1930, **63**, 1347; R. PALOMAA, *Ann. Acad. Sci. Fenn.*, 1911, A3, No. 2 (*Chem. Zent.*, 1912, **2**, 596); S. NIMS, *J. Amer. Chem. Soc.*, 1936, **58**, 987; T. DIPPY and WILLIAMS, *J. Chem. Soc.*, 1934, 161; U. DIPPY and LEWIS, ibid., 1937, 1008; V. IVES, LINSTEAD and WHITING, ibid., 1933, 561; W. MANSFIELD and WHITING, ibid., 1956, 4761; X. KILPATRICK and MORSE, *J. Amer. Chem. Soc.*, 1953, **75**, 1854; Y. DIPPY, HUGHES and LAXTON, *J. Chem. Soc.*, 1954, 4102.

properties, and hence the strength of benzoic acid is decreased by a methyl-group in the para position even more than in the meta position. Again the nitro-, cyano- and acetyl-groups have −I and −T properties, and hence the strength of benzoic acid is increased by these groups in the para position even more than in the meta position. In the more complicated case where a group has

—I and +T properties, the electron-withdrawing effects are less in the para than in the meta position, as is found for the hydroxy-, methoxy-, methylthio- and halogen substituents. For the hydroxy- and methoxy-substituents, the +T effect is so much more powerful than the —I effect that they actually have an acid-weakening effect in the para position (the hydroxy-benzoic acids are in Table 8.6).

The effects of several groups in the meta and para positions are numerically additive.

The ortho position is the most complicated of all. In almost every set of isomers the ortho is the strongest acid, and even when a substituent has both +I and +T properties (e.g. the methyl-group), the resultant acid is stronger than benzoic acid. The ortho position must receive the strongest I effects in any set of isomers, because the distance is least. Again, like the para position, and unlike the meta, it is capable of propagating T effects. However a further powerful effect is at work, and this is acid-strengthening. This third effect is believed to be a steric pressure exerted by the substituent group upon the carboxyl-group, so that the latter is forced out of the plane of the ring. As a result of this distortion, the acid-weakening +T effect of the benzene ring is decreased, i.e. the pK_a becomes referable to that of formic acid as modified by the inductive effect of the ortho substituent. The outstanding anomaly (*o*-acetylbenzoic acid) is explicable if the carboxyl-group can push the more flexible acetyl-group out of the way.

The aliphatic hydroxylic acids

The pK_a of water, ionizing as an acid, is 15·74 at 25°, calculated as 14 plus log 55·5 (55·5 is the molarity of water, viz. 1000/18). Recent careful measurements showed that methanol is a slightly stronger acid than water, whereas ethanol appears to be weaker. The usual —I substituents provide a range of more acidic alcohols down to pK 12·2 (see Table 8.3).

The aldehydes are monobasic acids owing to their existence, in solution, as 1,1-glycols, e.g. $CH_2(OH)_2$ for formaldehyde. The latter, and chloral, are completely hydrated in solution, but alde-

TABLE 8.2

Aromatic carboxylic acids (monobasic)
(in water)

Abbreviations for methods: as Table 8.1, *also* S, spectrometric.

Acid	pK_a			°C	Method	Ref.
Benzoic acid	$\begin{cases}4\cdot17\\4\cdot18\end{cases}$			25 25	P_QT CT	A B
2,4,6-Trinitro-	0·65			25	CT	O
	o-	*m-*	*p-*			
Methyl-	3·91	4·27	4·37	25	CT	C, F
Nitro-	2·17	3·49	3·43	25	CT	C, F
Sulphamyl- (–SO_2NH_2)	—	3·54	3·47	25	PT	J
Cyano-	—	3·60	3·55	20	P_QT	H
Fluoro-	3·27	3·87	4·14	25	CT	C, D
Chloro-	2·94	3·83	3·98	25	CT	D
Bromo-	2·85	3·81	3·97	25	CT	D
Iodo-	2·86	3·85	3·93	25	CT, ST	C, E
Acetyl-	4·13	3·83	3·70	25	CT	G
Phenoxy-	3·53	3·95	4·52	25	CT	F
Acetoxy- (–O.$COCH_3$)	3·48	4·00	4·38	25	C	I
Methoxy-	4·09	4·09	4·47	25	CT	C, F, P
Acetamido- (–NH.$COCH_3$)	3·63	4·07	4·28	25	C	I
Phenyl-	3·46	—	—	25	CT	F
	1-	2-				
Naphthoic acids	3·70	4·16		25	CT	N
	2-	3-				
Heterocyclic acids						
Furan–carboxylic	3·16	3·95		25	PT, P	K, L
Thiophen–carboxylic	3·53	4·10		30	PT, C	K, M
Pyrrole–carboxylic	4·45	—		25	P	

A. KOLTHOFF and BOSCH, *J. Phys. Chem.*, 1932, **36**, 1695; B. IVES, *J. Chem. Soc.*, 1933, 731; C. DIPPY and LEWIS, ibid., 1936, 644; D. DIPPY, WILLIAMS and LEWIS, ibid., 1935, 343; E. ROBINSON and ANG, ibid., 1959, 2314; F. DIPPY and LEWIS, ibid., 1937, 1426; G. BRAY, DIPPY and HUGHES, ibid., 1957, 265; H. BRIEGLEB and BIEBER, *Z. Elekt.*, 1951, **55**, 250; I. OSTWALD, *Z. phys. Chem.*, 1889, **3**, 369; J. ZOLLINGER and WITTWER, *Helv. chim. Acta*, 1956, **39**, 347; K. LUMME, *Suomen Kemistilehti*, 1960, **33**, 87; L. CATLIN, *Iowa State Coll. J. Sci.*, 1935, **10**, 65; M. VOERMAN, *Rec. Trav. Chim.*, 1907, **26**, 293; N. DIPPY, HUGHES and LAXTON, *J. Chem. Soc.*, 1954, 1470; O. DIPPY, HUGHES and LAXTON, ibid., 1956, 2995; P. DIPPY and WILLIAMS, ibid., 1934, 1888.

hydes with +I substituents (e.g. acetaldehyde) are only partly hydrated; hence the constant for acetaldehyde in Table 8.3 refers to the equilibrium:

$$\frac{[CH_3 . CH(OH)O^-][H^+]}{[R . CHO] + [R . CH(OH_2)]}$$

Acetone has no detectable acidic properties, but enolizable ketones are highly acidic. The figures given in Table 8.3 are for the true enol. For acetylacetone and benzoylacetone, which enolize only slowly, total pK_a values of 8·94 and 8·70 respectively were first found, corresponding to the equilibrium:

$$\frac{[enolate^-][H^+]}{[keto\text{-}form] + [enol\text{-}form]}$$

These figures were then adjusted for the percentage of enol present, as found by titration.

Phenols

The increased acidic strength of phenol, as compared to the aliphatic alcohols, is usually attributed to the combined effect of the electron-attracting inductive effect $(-I)$ of the benzene ring, and the resonance effect in the anion $(-I)$, shown as A. As both effects have the same sign, the increase in acid strength is large. This is quite different from what occurs in the benzoate anion where the $(-I)$ and $(+I)$ effects almost neutralize one another.

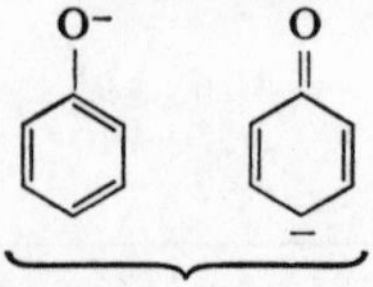

A

As in the benzoic acids, the meta position gives a clear picture of what inductive effects are operating. Thus the methyl-group is seen to be $(+I)$, and all other substituents shown in Table 8.4 are $(-I)$. The para position permits tautomeric, as well as inductive, effects. As before, where both effects have the same sign, the para position elicits a greater effect from the substituent than is possible

TABLE 8.3

Aliphatic hydroxylic acids (monobasic)

(in water)

Abbreviations for methods: As Table 8.1, also: P_{RF}, potentiometry by the rapid flow method; S, spectrometry; FP, freezing-point depression.

Acid	Substituent	pK_a	°C	Method	Ref.
Substituted methanols					
Methanol	H–	15·5			
Allyl alcohol	CH_2=CH–	15·5			
Glycol	$HO.CH_2$–	15·1			
Glycol methyl ether	$CH_3O.CH_2$–	14·8	25	CT	A
Propargyl alcohol	CH≡C–	13·6			
Trifluoroethanol	CF_3–	12·37			
Trichloroethanol	CCl_3–	12·24			
Mannitol		13·5	18	PT	B
Aldehydes and related substances					
Formaldehyde		13·7	18	C	C
		13·9	1	FP	D
Acetaldehyde		14·5	18, 1	C, FP	E
Chloral		11·3	18	C	E
Glucose		12·43	18	PT	B
		12·2	23	CT	F
Sucrose		12·7	23	CT	F
Pyridine-4-aldehyde		12·20	20	S	G
Glutaconic dialdehyde					
(⁻OCH=CH—CH=CH—CHO)		5·75	25	PT	H
Enolizable ketones					
Ethyl acetoacetate		10·68	25	$P^{0.009}$	I
Acetylacetone		8·24	25	$P_{RF}T$	H
		8·16	25	$P^{0.003}$	I
Benzoylacetone		8·23	25	$P^{0.002}$	I
Dihydroresorcinol		5·26	25	PT	H
Triacetylmethane		5·81	25	PT	H
Diacetylacetone		7·42	25	PT	H

A. BALLINGER and LONG, *J. Amer. Chem. Soc.*, 1960, **82**, 795; B. THAMSEN, *Acta Chem. Scand.*, 1952, **6**, 270; C. AUERBACH, *Ber.*, 1905, **38**, 2833; D. EULER, ibid., p. 2551; E. EULER, ibid., 1906, **39**, 344; F. STEARN, *J. Phys. Chem.*, 1931, **35**, 2226; G. NAKAMOTO and MARTELL, *J. Amer. Chem. Soc.*, 1959, **81**, 5857; H. SCHWARZENBACH and LUTZ, *Helv. chim. Acta*, 1940, **23**, 1147, 1162; I. EIDINOFF, *J. Amer. Chem. Soc.*, 1945, **67**, 2072, 2073.

TABLE 8.4

Phenols (monobasic) (in water)

Abbreviations for methods: As Table 8.1, also: S, spectroscopic;
I, indicator.

Acid		pK_a		°C	Method	Ref.
	o-	*m-*	*p-*			
Phenol 9·98				25	P[0·02]	A
Methyl- (cresol)	10·28	10·08	10·14	25, 25, 20	ST, P, P	N, A, M
Nitro-	7·23	8·40	7·15	25	CT, ST, ST	C, B, D
Cyano-	—	8·61	7·95	25	ST, PT	L, E
Methylsulphonyl- (CH_3SO_2-)	—	8·40[a]	7·83	25	P[0·02]	A
Formyl- (hydroxy-benzaldehyde)	8·37	9·02	7·62	25	ST	F
Acetyl- (hydroxy-acetophenone)	—	9·19	8·05	25	P[0·02]	A
Methoxycarbonyl- (CH_3O_2C-)	—	—	8·47	25	ST	G
Fluoro-	8·81	9·28	9·95	25	PT	H
Chloro-	8·48	9·02	9·38	25	S	I
Bromo-	8·44	9·03	9·36	25	ST	O
Iodo-	8·51	9·06	9·31	25	ST	O
Methylthio- (CH_3S-)	—	9·53	9·53	25	P[0·02]	A
Methoxy-	9·98	9·65	10·21	25	ST	B
Phenyl-	9·97	9·63	9·55	23	S	J
Trinitro- (picric acid) 0·71	←			25	CT	C
1-Naphthol 9·85				20	I[b]	K
2-Naphthol 9·63				20	PT	M

[a] Published as 9·33, later corrected by authors. [b] Phenol, by same method, 9·95.

A. BORDWELL and COOPER, *J. Amer. Chem. Soc.*, 1952, **74**, 1058; B. BIGGS, *Trans. Farad. Soc.*, 1956, **52**, 35; C. DIPPY, HUGHES and LAXTON, *J. Chem. Soc.*, 1956, 2995; D. ROBINSON and BIGGS, *Trans. Farad. Soc.*, 1955, **51**, 901; E. WHELAND, BROWNELL and MAYO, *J. Amer. Chem. Soc.*, 1948, **70**, 2492; F. ROBINSON and KIANG, *Trans. Farad. Soc.*, 1956, **52**, 327; G. SAGER, SCHOOLEY, CARR and ACREE, *J. Res. Nat. Bur. Standards*, 1945, **35**, 521; H. BENNETT, BROOKS and GLASSTONE, *J. Chem. Soc.*, 1935, 1821; I. JUDSON and KILPATRICK, *J. Amer. Chem. Soc.*, 1949, **71**, 3110; J. KIEFFER and RUMPF, *Compt. rendus*, 1954, **238**, 360; K. LAUER, *Ber.*, 1937, **70**, 1127; L. FICKLING, FISCHER, MANN, PACKER and VAUGHAN, *J. Amer. Chem. Soc.*, 1959, **81**, 4226; M. This book, p. 61; N. SPRENGLING and LEWIS, *J. Amer. Chem. Soc.*, 1953, **75**, 5709; O. BIGGS and ROBINSON, *J. Chem. Soc.*, 1961, 389.

in the meta position. For groups, like $-NO_2$, $-CN$ and $-SO_2CH_3$, which are $(-I, -T)$, some striking low pK_a values are reached, because the tautomeric potentialities of the phenol anion are so much greater than those of the benzoate anion, and the direction of the polarity is highly favourable. Where the I and T effects have opposite signs as in the halogens and in the methoxy-group, the relative strength of these effects can be gauged by the effect on acid strength. Thus $-F$ and, particularly, $-OMe$, have powerful $(+T)$ effects, running counter to the $(-I)$ effect.

The ortho position is much less subject to steric hindrance of the kind noted in the substituted benzoic acids.

Phenol, the naphthols, and 1- and 2-anthrol all have very similar acid strengths.

Diphenols, phenolcarboxylic acids and phenol sulphonic acids will be found in Table 8.6. Aminophenols and the hydroxy-derivatives of heterocyclic bases are in Table 8.13.

Miscellaneous oxygen acids

It is clear from studies with indicators, that methane sulphonic acid has a pK_a about 0 and is almost as strong as nitric acid.* The aryl-sulphonic acids are usually credited with pK_a values in the neighbourhood of 0·6,† and this seems reasonable but confirmation is desirable. Values for aryl-sulphinic and boric acids will be found in Table 8.5, and -phosphonic acids in Table 8.6. Sulphonic acids with a second ionizing group (e.g. $-OH$ or $-CO_2H$) are in Table 8.6, and aminosulphonic acids in Table 8.13.

The remaining acids in this section contain nitrogen, but it is reasonable to suppose that the oxygen atom is the principal carrier of the negative charge. The acid amides are very weak acids (see Table 8.5), and urea is said to have no detectable acidic properties.‡ However, a negative inductive effect strengthens the acid properties of acetamide greatly (see N-cyanoacetamide). Some hydroxamic acids and oximes have also been included in Table 8.5.

* BASCOMBE and BELL, *J. Chem. Soc.*, 1959, 1096.
† e.g. 0·74 (C, 25°) for naphthalene-1-sulphonic acid, FIERZ and WEISSENBACH, *Helv. chim. Acta*, 1920, **3**, 305.
‡ BELL, GILLESPIE and TAYLOR, *Trans. Farad. Soc.*, 1943, **39**, 137.

For nitroparaffins, the equilibrium commonly measured is as (I), and constants for this are in Table (8.5). This is a slow ionization, involving the loss of a proton from a carbon atom (the negative charge finally rests on oxygen). Rapid back-titration reveals the equilibrium (II) for which nitroethane gives pK_a 4·4.

$$\frac{[CH_3CH:NO_2^-][H^+]}{[CH_3CH_2NO_2]}$$

(I)

$$\frac{[CH_3CH:NO_2^-][H^+]}{[CH_3CH_2:NO_2H]}$$

(II)

TABLE 8.5

Miscellaneous oxygen acids

(in water)

Abbreviations for methods: As Table 8.1, also: Y, catalytic.

Acid	pK_a	°C	Method	Ref.
Benzenesulphinic acid	1·5	25	C	A
p-Toluenesulphinic acid	1·7	25	C	A
Phenylboric acid	8·86	25	P	B
β-Phenylethylboric acid	10·0	25	P	B
Acetamide	15·1	25	C	C
Benzamide	13–14	25	C	C
N-cyanoacetamide	4	?	?	D
Succinimide	9·62	25	P	E
Glutarimide	11·43	25	P	F
Acethydroxamic acid ($CH_3CONH.OH$)	9·40	20	$P^{0.01}$	G
Benzhydroxamic acid	8·89	20	$P^{0.01}$	G
Acetoxime (($CH_3)_2C:NOH$)	12·42	25	YT	H
Nitromethane (see text)	10·21	25	P	I
Nitroethane	8·44	25	P	I
Cyanic acid	3·7	25	K	J

A. COATS and GIBSON, *J. Chem. Soc.*, 1940, 442; B. YABROFF, BRANCH and BETTMAN, *J. Amer. Chem. Soc.*, 1934, **56**, 1850; C. BRANCH and CLAYTON, ibid., 1928, **50**, 1680; D. quoted in BRANCH and CALVIN, *The Theory. of Organic Chemistry*, New York: Prentice-Hall, 1941; E. WALTON and SCHILT, *J. Amer. Chem. Soc.*, 1952, **74**, 4995; F. SCHWARZENBACH and LUTZ, *Helv. chim. Acta*, 1940, **23**, 1162. G. WISE and BRANDT, *J. Amer. Chem. Soc.*, 1955, **77**, 1058; H. KING and MARION, ibid., 1944, **66**, 977; I. WHELAND and FARR, ibid., 1943, **65**, 1433; TURNBULL and MARON, ibid., p. 212. J. LISTER, *Canad. J. Chem.*, 1955, **33**, 426.

II. The oxygen acids (dibasic)

When a symmetrical molecule with two identical ionizable groups is progressively neutralized, two well-separated constants are produced. In the first step of ionization, the equilibrium (I) can lose a proton from two positions, but it can add a proton to only one position. The second stage of neutralization (II) can lose a proton from only one position, but can add it to two positions. Thus equilibrium (I) is statistically four times as favoured as equilibrium (II).

$$\text{(I)} \quad HO_2C.(CH_2)_4.CO_2H \rightleftharpoons HO_2C.(CH_2)_4.CO_2^- + H^+$$
$$\text{(II)} \quad HO_2C.(CH_2)_4.CO_2^- \rightleftharpoons {}^-O_2C.(CH_2)_4.CO_2^- + H^+$$

Because of the coulombic effect, the two constants of a symmetrical acid or base differ by *more* than this factor of four. Thus, the negative charge in (I) must repel the similarly charged hydroxyl ions in the ionic atmosphere. Hence it is necessary to increase the concentration of hydroxyl ions (i.e. to increase the pH) very much more for stage (II) than for stage (1).

Table 8.6 gives examples of several dibasic acids, and it is evident that the difference between pK_a^1 and pK_a^2 can be as little as 0.8 unit of pK, or more than 10 units. Much depends on whether the two similar charges are near or distant, mutually hydrogen bonded or free. It also matters whether the coulombic effect is exerted through water (as in a long, thin molecule) or through the molecule itself (as in a short, thick molecule) because the dielectric constants would be 80 and about 2, respectively. The extraordinary difference between pK_a^1 and pK_a^2 of salicylic acid is ascribed to hydrogen bonding of the first anion.

III. Sulphur acids

The high acidity of hydrogen sulphide (pK_a 7·02), relative to that of water, suggests that mercaptans would be more acidic than the corresponding alcohols. A selection of values determined directly in water is given in Table 8.7. It will be noted that thiophenol is a much stronger acid than phenol.

Sulphonic and sulphinic acids were dealt with on p. 131.

TABLE 8.6

Polybasic oxygen acids

(in water)

Abbreviation for methods: As Table 8.1, also: S, spectrometry.

Acid	pK$_a$	°C	Method	Ref.
Dibasic oxygen acids				
Oxalic acid	$\begin{cases} 1\cdot271 \\ 4\cdot266 \end{cases}$	25 25	CT PT	A B
Malonic	$\begin{cases} 2\cdot86 \\ 5\cdot70 \end{cases}$	25 25	CT PT	C D
Succinic	4·21, 5·64	25	PT	E
Glutaric	4·34, 5·27	25	P$^{0\cdot007}$	F
Adipic	4·41, 5·28	25	P$^{0\cdot007}$	F
Oxaloacetic	2·56, 4·37	25	PT	G
Maleic	1·92, 6·23	25	P$_Q$T	H
Fumaric	3·02, 4·38	25	P$_Q$T	H
Tartaric	3·03, 4·37	25	PT	I
o-Phthalic acid	$\begin{cases} 2\cdot950 \\ 5\cdot408 \end{cases}$	25	PT	J
m-isomer (isophthalic)	3·62, 4·60	25 ± 1	ST	K
p-isomer (terephthalic)	3·54, 4·46	25 ± 1	ST	K
o-Dihydroxybenzene (catechol)	9·45, (12·8)[a]	25	PT	L
m-isomer (resorcinol)	9·44	18	C	M
p-isomer (quinol)	9·96	18	C	M
o-Carboxyphenol (*o*-hydroxy-benzoic acid; salicylic acid)	$\begin{cases} 3\cdot00 \\ 13\cdot82 \end{cases}$	25 20	CT S$^{1\cdot23}$	N O
m-isomer	4·08	25	CT	N
p-isomer	4·57, 9·46	25	PT	P
m-Sulphonbenzoic acid (HO$_3$S.C$_6$H$_4$.CO$_2$H)	(0·31),[a] 3·78	25	P$^{0\cdot004}$	Q
p-isomer	(0·37),[a] 3·72	25	P$^{0\cdot004}$	Q
m-Sulphonphenol	(0·39),[a] 9·07	25	P$^{0\cdot004}$	Q
p-isomer	(0·58),[a] 8·70	25	P$^{0\cdot004}$	Q
Methyl phosphate (CH$_3$OP(OH)$_2$O)	1·54, 6·31	25	P$^{0\cdot04}$	R
(Dimethyl phosphate for comparison)	(1·29)[a]	25	P$^{0\cdot04}$	R
Phenyl phosphonic acid (C$_6$H$_5$P(OH)$_2$O)	1·83, 7·07	25	P$^{0\cdot1}$	S

Acid	pK$_a$	°C	Method	Ref.
Acids of basicity higher than 2				
Citric acid, 3·128, 4·761, 6·396	←	25	PT	T
Benzene-hexacarboxylic acid (mellitic), 1·40, 2·19, 3·31, 4·78, 5·89, 6·96	←	25	P$_Q$$^{0·03}$	U

[a] These values were obtained at such low concentrations that they may be 'mirages' (see p. 41).

A. DARKEN, *J. Amer. Chem. Soc.*, 1941, **63**, 1007; B. PINCHING and BATES, *J. Res. Nat. Bur. Standards*, 1948, **40**, 405; C. JEFFREY and VOGEL, *J. Chem. Soc.*, 1935, 21; D. HAMER, BURTON and ACREE, *J. Res. Nat. Bur. Standards*, 1940, **24**, 269; E. PINCHING and BATES, ibid., 1950, **45**, 322, 444; F. GANE and INGOLD, *J. Chem. Soc.*, 1928, 1594; G. PEDERSEN, *Acta Chem. Scand.*, 1952, **6**, 243; H. GERMAN, JEFFREY and VOGEL, *Phil. Mag.*, 1936, **22**, 790; I. BATES and CANHAM, *J. Res. Nat. Bur. Standards*, 1951, **47**, 343; J. HAMER, PINCHING and ACREE, ibid., 1945, **35**, 381, 539; K. THAMER and VOIGT, *J. Phys. Chem.*, 1952, **56**, 225; L. TIMBERLAKE, *J. Chem. Soc.*, 1957, 4987; M. EULER and BOLIN, *Z. physik. Chem.*, 1909, **66**, 71; N. BRAY, DIPPY, HUGHES and LAXTON, *J. Chem. Soc.*, 1957, 2405; O. This book, p. 41; P. SAGER, SCHOOLEY, CARR and ACREE, *J. Res. Nat. Bur. Standards*, 1945, **35**, 521; Q. ZOLLINGER, BÜCHLER and WITTWER, *Helv. Chim Acta*, 1953, **36**, 1711; R. KUMLER and EILER, *J. Amer. Chem. Soc.*, 1943, **65**, 2355; S. JAFFÉ, FREEDMAN and DOAK, ibid., 1953, **75**, 2209; T. BATES and PINCHING, ibid., 1949, **71**, 1274; U. MAXWELL and PARTINGTON, *Trans. Farad. Soc.*, 1937, **33**, 670.

TABLE 8.7

Sulphur acids (in water)

Acid		pK$_a$	°C	Method	Ref.
Ethyl mercaptan (C$_2$H$_5$SH)		10·50	20	P$^{0·01}$	A
β-Hydroxyethyl mercaptan		9·43	25	PT	B
Benzyl mercaptan		9·43	25	S	B
Phenyl mercaptan (thiophenol)		6·5[a]	25	S	B
Thioglycollic acid	{–SH	10·40	20	S	A
	{–CO$_2$H	3·68	25	C	C
Methyl thioglycollate		7·68	20	P$^{0·01}$	A
2-Mercaptopropionic acid	{–SH	10·20	20	P$^{0·01}$	A
	{–CO$_2$H	4·32	25	C	C
2-Mercaptoethane sulphonic acid		9·5	20	P$^{0·01}$	A

[a] Our own trials suggest that this figure is preferable to the 7·78 of Ref. A.

A. DANEHY and NOEL, *J. Amer. Chem. Soc.*, 1960, **82**, 2511; B. KREEVOY, HARPER, DUVALL, WILGUS and [DITSCH, ibid., p. 4899; C. LARSSON, *Z. Anorg. chem.*, 1928, **172**, 375.

IV. Nitrogen acids

The acidic nature of ammonia, well known from the commercial availability of sodamide, has been assigned a theoretically calculated pK_a of about 35.* The introduction of electron-attracting groups can lower this drastically, as shown in Table 8.8. The pK_a of nitramide $NO_2.NH_2$ from Table 8.14 is also of interest here.

TABLE 8.8

Nitrogen acids

(in water)

Abbreviations for methods: As Table 8.1, also: I, indicator method.

Acid	pK_a	°C	Method	Ref.
Aniline	27^a	25	I	A
Cyanamide $CN.NH_2$	10·27	25	C	C
Dicyanamide $(CN)_2NH$	~1	—	—	D
Dipicrylamine (hexanitrodiphenylamine)	5·42	25	P	B

a This value is merely indicative.

A. CONANT and WHELAND, *J. Amer. Chem. Soc.*, 1932, **54**, 1212; B. PAN and LIN, *J. Chinese Chem. Soc.*, 1955, II, **2**, 1 (*Chem. Abs.*, 1955, **49**, 14534); C. KAMEYAMA, *Trans. Amer. Electrochem. Soc.*, 1921, **40**, 131; D. BRANCH and CALVIN, *The Theory of Organic Chemistry*. New York: Prentice Hall, 1941.

V. Carbon acids

Carbanions are often invoked to explain inorganic reactions, but few have more than a transitory existence. However, the substitution of two, or more, strongly electron-attracting substituents into methane give stable acids, some of which are said to be as strong as mineral acids (see Table 8.9). For nitromethane, see Table 8.5. A number of hydrocarbons, roughly graded for acid strength by an indicator method, produced such figures as indene

* PLESKOV and MONOSZON, *Acta Physio-Chim. U.S.S.R.*, 1935, **1**, 725. Bell, *The Proton in Chemistry*. Methuen: London, 1960.

400 Typical Acids and Bases: Organic

(pK$_a$ 21), fluorene (25) and triphenylmethane (33). These figures,* are only relative, but it is notable that totally aromatic six-membered ring hydrocarbons were found to be even less acidic than triphenylmethane. Fluoradene (indenofluorene) has pK$_a$ 11 and hence it is exceptionally strong for a substance composed entirely of carbon and hydrogen.†

TABLE 8.9

Carbon acids

(in water)

Abbreviations for methods: As Table 8.1, also: Y, catalytic.

Acid	pK$_a$	°C	Method	Ref.
Diethyl malonate CH$_2$(CO$_2$C$_2$H$_5$)$_2$	13·3	?	?	A
Malonitrile CH$_2$(CN)$_2$	11·19	25	P	B
Cyanoform CH(CN)$_3$	<1	25	C	C
*Tris*ethylsulphonylmethane CH(SO$_2$C$_2$H$_5$)$_3$	<1	25	P, Y	D

A. PEARSON and MILLS, *J. Amer. Chem. Soc.*, 1950, **72**, 1692; B. PEARSON and DILLON, ibid., 1953, **75**, 2439; C. BIRKENBACH and HUTTNER, *Ber.*, 1929, **62**, 153; D. SAMÉN, *Arkiv Kemi Mineral. Geol.*, 1947, **24B**, No. 6 (*Chem. Abs.*, 1948, **42**, 6313).

VI. Nitrogen bases (monoacidic)

Aliphatic bases

When ammonia (pK$_a$ 9·25) is substituted by one alkyl-group, the pK$_a$ rises to 10·6, a value which remains steady no matter how large the alkyl-group (see Table 8·10). When a second alkyl-group is added, the second increase in basic strength is much smaller, and a third alkyl-group actually lowers the pK$_a$ to a value intermediate between that of the secondary amine and ammonia. The increases in basic strength following the first two alkylations of ammonia are derived from the inductive effect (+I) of the alkyl-group. The decrease following the third alkylation (as in tri-

* CONANT and WHELAND, *J. Amer. Chem. Soc.*, 1932, **54**, 1212.
† RAPOPORT and SMOLINSKY, *J. Amer. Chem. Soc.*, 1958, **80**, 2910.

methylamine) has been attributed to 'back-strain', a form of overcrowding,* but the most widely held opinion is that progressive alkylation of an amine must eventually reduce its strength by decreasing the number of hydrogen atoms (in the cation) capable of forming stabilizing hydrogen bonds with water.†

Tetra-alkylation, to give a quaternary salt, causes an immense increase in basic strength. In general, tetra-alkylammonium salts are completely ionized at all concentrations so far measured, hence no pK_a values have yet been assigned to them. If the nitrogen atom, as is generally believed, is incapable of forming five covalent bonds, no neutral molecule corresponding to a tetra-alkylammonium salt is conceivable. The low strength of ammonium salts, other than quaternary, is due to hydrogen-bonding to water molecules by lone pairs of electrons on the nitrogen atom in the neutral molecule.‡ Tetra-alkylammonium salts do not possess any such lone pair.

The effect on pK_a of substituents on the α-carbon atom of methylamine, and the β-carbon atom of ethylamine, are shown in Table 8.10. The effects are all inductive and the substituents behave very much as with acetic acid (Table 8.1). However, far fewer pK_a values of substituted bases have been determined than of substituted acids.

The value for allylamine raises the question of what would be the effect of moving the double-bond one place towards the nitrogen atom. Although simple aliphatic examples have not been measured, the phenomenon can be examined in the tetrahydropyridines and dihydropyrroles‖ which are essentially comparable.

Amidines and guanidines, thanks to extra resonance in the cations, are stronger bases than the simple aliphatic amines. At the other end of the scale are the amides which have only feebly basic properties. As the amides present difficulty in measurement, results from various methods are included in the table.

* BROWN, BARTHOLOMAY and TAYLOR, *J. Amer. Chem. Soc.*, 1944, **66**, 435.

† Bell, *The Proton in Chemistry*. Methuen: London, 1960.

‡ SIDGWICK, *The Organic Chemistry of Nitrogen*. Oxford, 1937.

‖ ADAMS and MAHAN, *J. Amer. Chem. Soc.*, 1942, **64**, 2588.

A selection of pK_a values of heteroaliphatic bases completes Table 8.10. For methyl-derivatives of hydroxylamine see Table 8.15. For the ionization constants of related alkaloids see Kolthoff.*

Aromatic bases

Aniline (pK_a 4·6) is a very much weaker base than either its saturated analogue (cyclohexylamine) or the aliphatic bases. This weakness is often attributed to a resonance (III) ↔ (IV) in the neutral molecule which is not possible in the ion. It is not usual for a mere separation of opposite charges in a neutral molecule to affect acidic or basic strength so markedly: moreover the dipole moment of aniline is only 1·6 D. Some evidence† has been offered that about half of the base-weakening effect in aniline comes from the −I inductive effect of the benzene ring which has the same sign as the resonance effect (−T). In benzoic acid, on the other hand, the two effects have opposite signs.

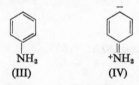

NH₂   +NH₂
(III)   (IV)

The reality of the base-weakening resonance in aniline is shown by N-alkyl substituents (see Table 8.11). N-Ethyl-substituents increase basic strength by more than could be expected from their +I effect, and are apparently, by their bulk, twisting the amino-group out of the plane of the benzene ring, a process which interferes with the base-weakening resonance. That this interpretation is correct is confirmed by the greater basic strength of N-*tert*butylaniline ($pK_a = 7·1$). Alkyl substituents, if placed ortho to the amino-group, lower basic strength by hindering the approach of the hydrated proton, cf. 2-*tert*butylaniline,‡ $pK_a = 3·8$.

* KOLTHOFF, *Biochem. Z.*, 1925, **162**, 289.
† WEPSTER, *Rec. Trav. Chim.*, 1952, 1159, 1171.
‡ 2,4,6-Tri*tert*butylaniline has pK_a <2 (BARTLETT, ROHA and STILES, *J. Amer. Chem. Soc.*, 1954, **76**, 2349).

TABLE 8.10

Aliphatic nitrogen and oxygen bases (monoacidic)

(in water)

Abbreviations for methods: As Table 8.1; also: S, spectrometry; P_A, potentiometry in acetic acid referred to water; D, distribution studies; Y, catalytic; Pol, polarography.

Base		pK_a	°C	Method	Ref.
Homologues and isomers					
Methylamine		10·62	25	P	A
Dimethylamine		10·77	25	P	A
Trimethylamine		9·80	25	P	A
Ethylamine		10·63	25	PT	B
Diethylamine		10·93	25	PT	B
Triethylamine		10·87	25	CT	C
n-Propylamine		10·53	25	PT	B
iso-Propylamine [$(CH_3)_2CH.NH_2$]		10·63	25	PT	D
n-Butylamine		10·60	25	PT	B
tert-Butylamine [$(CH_3)_3C.NH_2$]		10·45	25	PT	D
Octylamine		10·65	25	C	E
Undecylamine		10·63	25	C	E
Dodecylamine		10·63	25	C	E
Hexadecylamine		10·61	25	C	E
Docosylamine		10·60	25	C	E
Substituted methylamines (RCH_2NH_2)					
	R				
Methoxycarbonyl-	CH_3O_2C-	7·66	25	P	F
Carbamyl-	NH_2OC-	7·93	24	P	G
Phenyl- (benzylamine)	C_6H_5-	9·34	25	PT	D
Vinyl- (allylamine)	$H_2C:CH-$	9·69	25	C	H
Cyano-	$NC-$	5·34	25	P	I
Substituted ethylamines ($RCH_2CH_2NH_2$)					
Cyano-	$NC-$	7·7	29	P	I
Ethoxycarbonyl-	$C_2H_5O_2C-$	9·13	25	P	F
Hydroxy- (ethanolamine)	$HO-$	9·50	25	PT	J
Phenyl-	C_6H_5-	9·83	25	PT	D
Methoxy-	CH_3O-	9·45	25	P	K
Triethanolamine		7·82	22	PT	D
Cyclohexylamine		10·64	25	PT	D

Base	pK$_a$	°C	Method	Ref.
Acetamidine	12·40	25	PT	L
Benzamidine	11·6	20	P$^{0·1}$	O
Guanidine[a]	13·6	25	P$^{2·0}$	D, M
Diguanide				
H$_2$N.C(:NH).NH.C(:NH).NH$_2$	12·8	20–25	S	N
N-Acetylguanidine	8·33	20	P$^{0·05}$	O
N-Methylguanidine	13·4	25	P$^{1·0}$	M
NN-Dimethylguanidine	13·4	25	P$^{1·0}$	M
NN'-Dimethylguanidine	13·6	25	P$^{1·0}$	M
Amides				
Acetamide	−0·51	25	Y	P
	−0·48	25	P$_A$	R
Urea	0·18	25	Y	P
	0·31	21	P$^{0·5}$	Q
	0·10	25	P$_A$	R
O-Methyl*iso*urea	9·72	24	P	G
Thiourea	−0·96	25	Y	P
S-Methyl*iso*thiourea	9·83	20	P$^{0·03}$	O
Cyanamide (NC.NH$_2$)	1·1	29	P	I
Acethydrazide (CH$_3$CONH.NH$_2$)	3·24	24	P$^{0·1}$	S
Hetero-aliphatic bases				
Piperidine	11·22			
N-Methyl-	10·08			
Pyrrolidine	11·27	25	PT	U
N-Methyl-	10·46			
Azetidine	11·29			
Aziridine	8·04			
2-Methyl-Δ^2-tetrahydropyridine	9·57	24	P$^{0·08}$	T
Morpholine	8·70	25	P	K
Imines				
Cyclohexanonimine	9·15	?	Pol	V
Diphenylketimine	6·82	20	P	W
Oxygen bases				
Diethyl ether	−3·59	R.T.	D	X
Dioxan	−2·92	R.T.	D	X
2,6-Dimethyl-4-pyrone	0·4	25	PA	R
Acetone	−7·2	25	S	Y
Cyclohexanone	−6·8	25	S	Y

[a] The second pK$_a$ of guanidine is about −11 (WILLIAMS and HARDY, *J. Chem. Soc.*, 1953, 2560).

A. EVERETT and WYNNE-JONES, *Proc. Roy. Soc.*, 1941, **A 177**, 499; B. EVANS and HAMANN, *Trans. Farad. Soc.*, 1951, **47**, 34; C. ABLARD, McKINNEY

Ionization Constants

In general, meta-substituted anilines show the usual inductive effects, already discussed in connexion with aromatic carboxylic acids (p. 123). These inductive effects usually influence the magnitude of the pK_a of aniline even more than they influence that of phenol (Table 8.4). In the para position, these inductive effects are reinforced by any tautomeric effect of which the substituent is capable, as explained on p. 123. The halogens and the methoxy-group show the usual resultant of $-I$ and $+T$ effects.

Table 8.11 also records the pK_a values of diphenylamine, acetanilide, the naphthylamines, and a small selection of hetero-aromatic bases (for other heterocyclic examples see *The Application of Physical Methods to Heterocyclic Chemistry*, Academic Press, 1962, Editor: Katritzky). It will be noted that a second ring-nitrogen atom depresses basic strength (by a $-I$ effect) except in a few cases where a base-strengthening resonance counteracts this effect (e.g. pyrazole, imidazole). Table 8.11 concludes with a selection of derivatives of pyridine. It will be seen that, in general, the effect of a substituent in pyridine is similar to its effect in aniline. However, there is almost no *ortho*-effect in pyridine because the cation-forming group does not project beyond the ring. For this reason, 2-substituted pyridines have

---

and WARNER, *J. Amer. Chem. Soc.*, 1940, **62**, 2181; D. HALL and SPRINKLE, ibid., 1932, **54**, 3469; E. HOERR, MCCORKLE and RALSTON, ibid., 1943, **65**, 328; F. EDSALL and BLANCHARD, ibid., 1933, **55**, 2337; G. ZIEFF and EDSALL, ibid., 1937, **59**, 2245; H. BREDIG, *Z. physik. Chem.*, 1894, **13**, 289; I. STEVENSON and WILLIAMSON, *J. Amer. Chem. Soc.*, 1958, **80**, 5943; SOLOWAY and LIPSCHITZ, *J. Org. Chem.*, 1958, **23**, 613; J. BATES and PINCHING, *J. Res. Nat. Bur. Standards*, 1951, **46**, 349; K. BRUEHLMAN and VERHOEK, *J. Amer. Chem. Soc.*, 1948, **70**, 1401; L. SCHWARZENBACH and LUTZ, *Helv. chim. Acta*, 1940, **23**, 1162; M. ANGYAL and WARBURTON, *J. Chem. Soc.*, 1951, 2492; N. GAGE, ibid., 1949, 221; O. ALBERT, GOLDACRE and PHILLIPS, ibid., 1948, 2240; P. LUNDÉN, *Z. physik. Chem.*, 1906, **54**, 532; Q. BELL, GILLESPIE and TAYLOR, *Trans. Farad. Soc.*, 1943, **39**, 137; R. HALL, *J. Amer. Chem. Soc.*, 1930, **52**, 5115; S. LINDEGREN and NIEMANN, ibid., 1949, **71**, 1504; T. ADAMS and MAHAN, ibid., 1942, **64**, 2588; U. SEARLES, TAMRES, BLOCK and QUARTERMAN, ibid., 1956, **78**, 4917; V. BREZINA and ZUMAN, *Chem. Listy*, 1953, **47**, 975 (per *Chem. Abs.*, 1954, **48**, 5674); W. CULBERTSON, *J. Amer. Chem. Soc.*, 1951, **73**, 4818; X. ARNETT and WU, ibid., 1960, **82**, 4999; Y. CAMPBELL and EDWARD, *Canad. J. Chem.*, 1960, **38**, 2109.

been much studied to throw light on the ortho position in benzene derivatives.

The 2- and 4-aminopyridines, and similarly substituted quinolines, acridines, etc. permit a resonance in the cation (V) ↔ (VI) which is not possible in the neutral molecule.* This resonance is base-strengthening, and very strongly so in the 4-position.

The basic strength of triphenylmethane dyes, such as crystal violet (VII), although complicated by carbinol formation, has been clarified. This work† should be consulted in connexion with the quaternary N-heterocycles, such as acridine methobromide, which behave similarly.

VII. Nitrogen bases (diacidic)

The relationship between the pK_a values of two basic groups in the same molecule is governed by the influences that control the relationship between two acidic groups in one molecule (see p. 133). Several examples of diacidic bases are given in Table 8.12. The aliphatic bases in this Table clearly show how an ionized amino-group has a much larger effect than a non-ionized amino-group on the ionization of the other amino-group. These effects fall off as the two amino-groups are separated by more and more carbon atoms, but the effect of the ionized amino-group persists further. Hence, in a homologous series, the bigger differences are found in the second ionization step (i.e. the weaker base, lower of the two figures).

* ALBERT, GOLDACRE and PHILLIPS, *J. Chem. Soc.*, 1948, 2240.
† GOLDACRE and PHILLIPS, *J. Chem. Soc.*, 1949, 1724.

TABLE 8.11

Aromatic and heteroaromatic nitrogen bases (monoacidic)

(in water)

Abbreviations for methods: As Table 8.1; plus I, indicator; S, spectrometric; D, distribution between solvents; Y, catalytic; P_A, potentiometry in acetic acid referred to water.

Base	pK$_a$			°C	Method	Ref.
Aniline	4·58			25	P	A
N-methyl-	4·85			25	P	A
N-dimethyl-	5·06			25	PT	A
N-ethyl-	5·11			25	P	A
N-diethyl	6·56			25	P	A
N-*iso*propyl-	5·50			25	P	B
N-*tert*butyl-	7·10			19	P$^{0·01}$	C
	o-	*m-*	*p-*			
Methyl- (toluidines)	4·39	4·69	5·12	25	PT	A
Nitro-	−0·29	2·50	1·02	25	IT	D
Cyano-	—	2·76	1·74	25	ST	E
Fluoro-	3·20	3·59	4·65	25	ST	M
Chloro-	2·64	3·34	3·98	25	I, I, ST	F, F, G
Bromo-	2·60	3·51	3·91	25	D	H
Iodo-	2·60	3·61	3·78	25	ST	M
Methoxycarbonyl- (CH_3O_2C-)	2·23	3·64	2·38	25	Y	I
Methylsulphonyl- (CH_3O_2S-)	—	2·68	1·48	25	P	J
Methylthio- (CH_3S-)	—	4·05	4·40	25	P	J
Methoxy-	4·49	4·20	5·29	25	PT	A
Ethoxy-	4·47	4·17	5·25	25	PT	A
Trifluoromethyl-	—	3·5	2·6	25	P	K
Phenyl-	3·78	4·18	4·27	25	P	A, L, A
	pK$_a$					
2,6-Dimethylaniline	3·89			25	P	N
2-*tert*-Butylaniline	3·78			25	P	N
N-Dimethyl-*o*-toluidine	5·86			25	PT	A
N-Diethyl-*o*-toluidine	7·18			25	P	A
Diphenylamine	0·9			25	P$_A$	O
Acetanilide	0·4			25	P$_A$	O

Base	pKa	°C	Method	Ref.
sym-Diphenylguanidine	10·12	25	P	A
1-Naphthylamine	3·92	25	PT	A
2-Naphthylamine	4·11	25	PT	A
Benzenediazonium ion ($C_6H_5N_2^+$)	11·08[a]	0	C	P
Heterocyclic bases (parent substances)				
Pyridine	5·23	20	$P^{0·017}$	S
Quinoline	4·94	20	$P^{0·017}$	S
Acridine	5·60	20	$S^{0·01}$	S
Pyridazine	2·33	20	$P^{0·1}$	S
Pyrimidine	1·30	20	$P^{0·07}$	S
Pyrazine	0·6	20	$P^{0·1}$	S
Phthalazine	3·47	20	$P^{0·012}$	S
Quinoxaline	0·72	20	PT	T
Phenazine	1·2	20	$S^{0·01}$	S
Pyrrole	−0·27	25	S	AA
Pyrazole	2·53	25	Y	U
Imidazole	7·03	25	PT	V
Thiazole	2·53	20	$P^{0·1}$	S
Benzimidazole	5·53	20	$P^{0·025}$	S
Benztriazole	1·6	20	$P^{0·05}$	S
Pyridines				
2-Methoxy-	3·28	20	$P^{0·01}$	W
3-Methoxy-	4·88	20	$S^{0·01}$	W
4-Methoxy-	6·62	20	$P^{0·02}$	W
2-Fluoro-	−0·44	25	S	X
2-Chloro-	+0·72	25	ST	X
2-Bromo-	0·90	25	ST	X
2-Iodo-	1·82	25	ST	X
3-Chloro-	2·84	25	ST	X
2-Methyl-	5·97	25	ST	Y
3-Methyl-	5·68	25	ST	Y
4-Methyl-	6·02	25	ST	Y
2-*tert*butyl-	5·76	25	ST	Y
3-Acetyl-	3·18	25	PT	A
3-Cyano-	1·45	24	$P^{0·04}$	Z
2-Amino-	6·86	20	$P^{0·017}$	S
3-Amino-	5·98	20	$P^{0·017}$	S
4-Amino-	9·17	20	$P^{0·02}$	S
Pyridine-N-oxide	0·79	24	S	Z

[a] equilibrium with diazo hydroxide

(References, p. 146)

145

The aromatic diamines present a slightly more complex picture because a base-strengthening ($+$T) effect is transmitted from a non-ionized amino-group in the ortho and para positions. In the ortho position, this is counteracted by the steric effect (p. 139) which is base-weakening.

Some aminopyridines, at the end of Table 8.11, may be of interest here, also. For hydrazines see Table 8.15.

VIII. Miscellaneous bases

Basic properties can originate in atoms other than nitrogen. The basic pK_a of the oxygen atom in ether is -3.6, and anisole -6.5. Some oxygen heterocycles are more basic because of resonance possibilities in the cation, e.g. γ-pyrone is $+0.3$, and anthocyanidin $+4$. A number of oxygen bases will be found at the end of Table 8.10.

Carbonium ions often play a transitory part in chemical reactions. Some stable carbonium ions are known, e.g. $2,4,2',4',2'',4''$-hexamethoxytriphenylcarbinol* which has a pK_a of $+3.2$.

Phenyl mercuric hydroxide† has pK_a 4.00 at $25°$.

Many of the so-called 'onium' bases behave like sodium hydrox-

A. HALL and SPRINKLE, *J. Amer. Chem. Soc.*, 1932, **54**, 3469; B. BADDELEY, CHADWICK and TAYLOR, *J. Chem. Soc.*, 1954, 2405; C. VEXLEARSCHI and RUMPF, *Compt. rendus*, 1949, **229**, 1152; D. BASCOMBE and BELL, *J. Chem. Soc.*, 1959, 1096; E. FICKLING, FISCHER, MANN, PACKER and VAUGHAN, *J. Amer. Chem. Soc.*, 1959, **81**, 4226; F. KILPATRICK and ARENBERG, ibid., 1953, **75**, 3812; G. BATES and SCHWARZENBACH, *Helv. chim. Acta*, 1954, **37**, 1069; H. FLÜRSCHEIM, *J. Chem. Soc.*, 1910, **97**, 96; I. JOHNSTON and CUMMING, *Z. physik. Chem.*, 1907, **57**, 557, 574; J. BORDWELL and COOPER, *J. Amer. Chem. Soc.*, 1952, **74**, 1058; K. ROBERTS, WEBB and McELHILL, ibid., 1950, **72**, 408; L. KIEFFER and RUMPF, *Compt. rendus*, 1950, **230**, 1874; M. BIGGS and ROBINSON, *J. Chem. Soc.*, 1961, 389; N. WEPSTER, *Rec. Trav. Chim.*, 1957, **76**, 357; O. HALL, *J. Amer. Chem. Soc.*, 1930, **52**, 5115; P. DAVIDSON and HANTZSCH, *Ber.*, 1898, **31**, 1612; S. ALBERT, GOLDACRE and PHILLIPS, *J. Chem. Soc.*, 1948, 2240; T. ALBERT, BROWN and WOOD, ibid., 1954, 3832; U. DEDICHEN, *Ber.*, 1906, **39**, 1831; V. KIRBY and NEUBERGER, *Biochem, J.*, 1938, **32**, 1146; W. ALBERT and PHILLIPS, *J. Chem. Soc.*, 1956, 1294; X, BROWN and McDANIEL, *J. Amer. Chem. Soc.*, 1955, 77, 3752; Y. BROWN and MIHM, ibid., p. 1723; Z. JAFFÉ and DOAK, ibid., p. 4441; A. A. NAQVI and FERNANDO, *J. Org. Chem.*, 1960, **25**, 551.

* KOLTHOFF, *J. Amer. Chem. Soc.*, 1927, **49**, 1218.
† WAUGH, WALTON and LASWICK, *J. Phys. Chem.*, 1955, **59**, 395.

TABLE 8.12

Nitrogen bases (diacidic)

(in water)

Abbreviations for methods: As Table 8.1, also: S, spectroscopy.

Bases	pK$_a$ 2H$^+$	pK$_a$ H$^+$	°C	Method	Ref.
Aliphatic					
1,2-Ethanediamine	7·00	10·09	20	PT	A
1,3-Propanediamine	8·64	10·62	20	PT	A
1,4-Butanediamine	9·35	10·80	20	PT	A
1,8-Octanediamine	(10·10)	11·00	20	P	B
cis-1,2-Cyclohexanediamine	6·43	9·93	20	PT	A
trans-1,2-Cyclohexanediamine	6·47	9·94	20	PT	A
1,3-Diamino-2-propanol	7·93	9·69	20	PT	A
Piperazine	(5·68)	9·82	20	P	C
Aromatic					
Benzidine	3·63	4·70	20	S$^{0.01}$	D
	(3·4)	(4·7)	?	P$^{0.008}$	E
o-Phenylenediamine	< 2	4·47	20	P	F
m-Phenylenediamine	(2·65)	4·88	20	P	F
p-Phenylenediamine	(3·29)	6·08	20	P	F
N,N'-Tetramethyl-*p*-phenylene-diamine	2·20	6·35	20	PT	G

A. BERTSCH, FERNELIUS and BLOCK, *J. Phys. Chem.*, 1958, **62**, 444; B. SCHWARZENBACH, *Helv. chim. Acta*, 1933, **16**, 522; C. SCHWARZENBACH, MAISSEN and ACKERMANN, ibid., 1952, **35**, 2333; D. This book, p. 90; E. RUMPF, *Compt. rendus*, 1934, **198**, 269; F. KUHN and ZUMSTEIN, *Ber.*, 1926, **59**, 488; KUHN and WASSERMANN, *Helv. chim. Acta*, 1928, **11**, 3; G. WILLI, ibid., 1957, **40**, 2019.

ide in conductivity measurements, and hence are highly ionized at all concentrations.* This family consists of cations of the type $^+R(CH_3)_4$ (ammonium, phosphonium, arsonium and stibonium), and of the type $^+R(CH_3)_3$ (sulphonium and telluronium), of the type $^+R(CH_3)_2$ (iodonium and thallonium). Analogues where tin or lead replace sulphur are much weaker bases.

* OSTWALD, *J. Pr. Chem.*, 1886, **33**, 352; BREDIG, *Z. phys. Chem.*, 1894, **13**, 289.

TABLE 8.13

Amphoteric substances

(in water)

Abbreviations for methods: As Table 8.1, also: S, spectrographic.

Substance	pK$_a$		°C	Method	Ref.
	proton gained	proton lost			
Aliphatic					
2-Aminoacetic acid (glycine)	2·22	9·86	20	P$^{0·01}$	A
2-Aminopropionic acid (alanine)	2·22	9·97	20	P$^{0·01}$	A
3-Aminopropionic acid (β-alanine)	3·60	10·36	20	P$^{0·01}$	A
5-Aminovaleric acid	4·27	10·77	25	P	B
2-Mercaptoethylamine	8·27	10·53	25	P	C
Aminomethanesulphonic acid ($NH_2CH_2SO_3H$)	?	5·75	?	P	D
Aminoethane-β-sulphonic acid (taurine)	1·5[a]	9·08	20	P	A, D
Aromatic					
2-Aminophenol	4·72	9·71	21	P	E
3-Aminophenol	4·17	9·87	21	P	E
4-Aminophenol	5·50	10·30	21	P	E
2-Aminobenzoic acid (anthranilic acid)	2·11	4·95	25	P	F
3-Aminobenzoic acid	3·12	4·74	25	P	F
4-Aminobenzoic acid	2·41	4·85	25	P	F
Aniline-3-sulphonic acid	0·39[a]	3·65	25	P$^{0·1}$	G
Aniline-4-sulphonic acid (sulphanilic acid)	0·58[a]	3·12	25	P$^{0·1}$	G
Heterocyclic					
Pyridine-2-carboxylic acid (picolinic acid)	1·06	5·37	25	PT	F
Pyridine-3-carboxylic acid (nicotinic acid)	2·07	4·73	25	PT	F
Pyridine-4-carboxylic acid (isonicotinic acid)	1·70	4·89	25	PT	F

| Substance | pK$_a$ | | °C | Method | Ref. |
	proton gained	proton lost			
2-Hydroxyquinoline	−0·31	11·74⎫		⎧S, P$^{0·005}$⎫	
3-Hydroxyquinoline	4·30	8·06⎪		⎪P$^{0·005}$⎪	
4-Hydroxyquinoline	2·27	11·25⎪		⎪P$^{0·01}$⎪	
5-Hydroxyquinoline	5·20	8·54⎬	20	⎨P$^{0·003}$⎬	H
6-Hydroxyquinoline	5·17	8·88⎪		⎪P$^{0·005}$⎪	
7-Hydroxyquinoline	5·48	8·85⎪		⎪P$^{0·003}$⎪	
8-Hydroxyquinoline	5·13	9·89⎭		⎩P$^{0·005}$⎭	
2-Mercaptoquinoline	−1·44	10·21⎫			
3-Mercaptoquinoline	2·33	6·13⎬	20	S	I
4-Mercaptoquinoline	0·77	8·83⎭			

ᵃ These values may be 'mirages' (see p. 41).

A. ALBERT, *Biochem. J.*, 1950, **47**, 531; B. NEUBERGER, *Proc. Roy. Soc.*, 1937, **A 158**, 68; C. FELDER, RESCIGNO and RADICE, *Gazz. chim. Ital.*, 1955, **85**, 453; D. RUMPF, *Bull. Soc. Chim. France*, 1938, **5**, 871; E. KUHN and WASSERMANN, *Helv. chim. Acta*, 1928, **11**, 3; F. LUMME, *Suomen Kem.*, 1957, **30B**, 173; G. ZOLLINGER, BÜCHLER and WITTWER, *Helv. chim. Acta*, 1953, **36**, 1711; H. ALBERT and PHILLIPS, *J. Chem. Soc.*, 1956, 1294; I. ALBERT and BARLIN, ibid., 1959, 2384.

IX. Amphoteric substances

The discussion on amphoteric substances in Chapter 7 (p. 113) will serve to introduce Table 8.13 which contains a number of typical examples.

Most of those amino-acids that are protein constituents have lower pK$_a$ values about 2·0, and upper values between 8 and 10 (some have two values in the 8–10 range). Histidine with pK$_a$ values of 1·8, 6·1 and 9·2 is a slight variant.

pK$_a$ values of thirteen naphthylaminesulphonic acids (proton lost constants only) are available* to supplement the aniline-sulphonic acids of Table 8.13).

* BRYSON, *Trans. Farad. Soc.*, 1951, **47**, 522.

B. INORGANIC SECTION

I. Inorganic acids

A number of inorganic acids are listed, in order of descending pK_a, in Table 8.14. All the values relate to water, but some of the extreme figures (e.g. NH_3 and HCl) have been obtained by theoretical estimation only and all work is not in agreement even on the order of magnitude. In any one column of the periodic table, acid strength increases with rising atomic number, at least for the simple hydrides (cf. H_2O, H_2S, H_2Se and H_2Te; again, cf. HF, HCl, HBr, HI). However, acid strength is not closely connected with electronegativity.

The strengths of oxy-acids increases with the number of oxygen atoms *not* linked to hydrogen (in the mono-anion). When there is only *one* such atom, the pK_a lies between 7 and 11. When there are *two* such oxygens, the pK_a is between 1 and 3·5; similarly *three* such ogygen atoms give values between pK_a -3 and -1. Perchloric acid, which is very strong, has four such atoms. Thus the mono-anion of phosphoric acid with two such oxygen atoms: $^-P(:O)_2$, $(OH)_2$, has a pK_a of 2·1. The di-anions can be similarly classified on a parallel scale. The values on this scale are higher, because the coulombic effect of one negative charge hinders the approach of hydroxyl ions, and hence makes the second ionization more difficult.

Some of the ionization constants in Table 8.14 are resultants of a true ionization constant and a dehydration constant (e.g. $HCO_3^- \rightleftharpoons H_2CO_3 \rightleftharpoons CO_2$, where the true pK_a is 3·8, i.e. it is actually 400 times stronger than a simple titration reveals). Periodic acid and telluric acid are also much weaker than would be expected because of hydration phenomena. Again, phosphorous and hypophosphorous acid can be fitted to the 'oxygen rule' only if it is remembered that they both have pentavalent phosphorus.

Some of the constants are known accurately, particularly when the partly neutralized acid is in common use as a buffer, but most of them are known only approximately. The temperature coefficients differ enormously, and are usually large.

TABLE 8.14

Inorganic acids

(in water)

Acid	pK$_a$	Acid	pK$_a$
Ammonia	33	Chloric acid	−1
Water	15·7	Chromic acid	−1, +6·5
Alumina	11·2	Nitric acid	−1·64
Hypoiodous acid	10	Permanganic acid	−2·3
Arsenious acid	9·6	Selenic acid	−3, +2
Boric acid	9·2	Sulphuric acid	−3, +2·0
[Hydrocyanic acid]	9·1	Hydrogen chloride	−7
Hypobromous acid	8·7	Perchloric acid	−8
Telluric acid	7·64	Hydrogen bromide	−9
Hypochlorous acid	7·3	Hydrogen iodide	−11
Hydrogen sulphide	7·0, 14·0		
[Carbonic acid]	6·4, 10·4		
Nitramide (NO$_2$.NH$_2$)	6·59		
Hydrogen selenide	4		
Hydrogen fluoride	3·18		
Hydrogen telluride	3		
Nitrous acid	3·4		
Chlorous acid	2		
Phosphoric acid	2·1, 7·2, 11·9		
Arsenic acid	2·3		
Phosphorous acid	1·8, 6·2		
Sulphurous acid	1·8, 7·2		
Periodic acid	1·55		
Hypophosphorous acid	1·1		
Pyrophosphoric acid	1, 2, 7, 9		
Iodic acid	0·77		

II. Inorganic bases

The pK$_a$ values of some inorganic bases related to ammonia are listed in Table 8.15. N-Methylation seems to cause steric hindrance to protonation, as in *o*-toluidine (p. 139). It is also possible to express the ionization of metal bases in the form of acidity constants following suggestions* that protons are derived from

* WERNER, *Ber.*, 1907, **40**, 272; PFEIFFER, ibid., 1907, **40**, 4036.

water molecules bound to metal ions. Thus the ionization of potassium hydroxide should be subject to this equilibrium:

$$K_a = \frac{[H^+][KOH]}{[K^+, H_2O]} \tag{8.1}$$

where K_a is termed the 'hydrolysis constant'.

It is true that we are usually more aware of the hydroxyl- than of the hydrogen-ion concentration in potassium hydroxide. However, equation (8.1) is of a kind which has proved very useful for organic bases, and it can also be used for inorganic bases, in the generalized form:

$$K_a = \frac{[H^+][MOH_{aq}^{(n-1)+}]}{[M_{aq}^{n+}]} \tag{8.2}$$

It is not easy to select, from a voluminous literature, many values that truly represent this simple equilibrium. Heavy metals often form polynuclear complexes, which involve new ionic species and complicate the equilibria. Thus the pK_a of cupric ion has been reported as 6·5 to 7·9, but meticulous study has shown that polynuclear complexes, especially $HO.Cu^+-Cu^+.OH$, are the main oxygen-containing species present.* At the other extreme, mercuric ion behaves in a perfectly orthodox way, giving $HOHg^+$ and $(HO)_2Hg$ with no signs of any polynuclear complex.† Ferric ion occupies an intermediate position. It must be emphasized that such studies must be made with a non-complexing anion, of which perchlorate is the best.

Many examples of apparent constancy of pK_a for cations is due to (*a*) an insufficient range of concentrations, or (*b*) failure to study the reaction up to a high degree of hydrolysis. Table 8.15 gives pK_a values for the first hydrolysis constant of those few metal ions for which there is sufficient evidence that only mononuclear species were present during the determination.

---

* PEDERSEN, *Kgl. Danske Videnskab. Selskab*, 1943, **20**, 7; PERRIN, *J. Chem. Soc.*, 1960, 3189.
† HIETANEN and SILLÉN, *Acta Chem. Scand.*, 1952, **6**, 747.

TABLE 8.15

Inorganic bases

(in water)

Base	pK$_a$	°C	Ref.
Nitrogen bases[a]			
Ammonia	9·27	25	A
Hydrazine	−0·88, 8·11	20	B
Methyl-	7·87	30	N
Tetramethyl-	6·30	30	N
Hydroxylamine	5·97	25	A
N-Dimethyl-	5·20	25	A
O-Methyl-	4·60	25	A
Trimethyl-	3·65	25	A
Heavy metals			
Manganous	10·6	30	C
Ferrous	9·5	25	D
Cadmium	9·0	25	E
Cobaltous	8·9	30	C
Mercurous	5·0	25	F
Mercuric	3·70	25	G
Thallic	1·14	25	H
Ferric (Fe^{+++} ⇌ FeOH^{++})	3·05	25	D
(FeOH^{++} ⇌ Fe(OH)$_2$$^+$)	3·26	25	D
Alkalies and alkaline earths			
Lithium	14·1[a]	25	I
Calcium	12·7[b, c]	25	J, K
Barium	13·4[b, d]	25	J, L
Magnesium	11·4[d]	25	M

[a] Conductimetry, [b] kinetic, [c] solubility, [d] potentiometric.

A. BISSOT, PARRY and CAMPBELL, *J. Amer. Chem. Soc.*, 1957, **79**, 796; B. SCHWARZENBACH, *Helv. chim. Acta*, 1936, **19**, 178; C. CHABEREK, COURTNEY and MARTELL, *J. Amer. Chem. Soc.*, 1952, **74**, 5057; D. HEDSTRÖM, *Arkiv. Kemi*, 1953, **5**, 457; **6**, 1; E. MARCUS, *Acta Chem. Scand.* 1957, **11**, 690; F. FORSLING, HIETANEN and SILLÉN, ibid., 1952, **6**, 901; G. HIETANEN and SILLÉN, ibid., p. 747; H. BIEDERMANN, *Rec. Trav. Chim.*, 1956, **75**, 716; I. DARKEN and MEIRS, *J. Amer. Chem. Soc.*, 1942, **64**, 621; J. BELL and PRUE, *J. Chem. Soc.*, 1949, 362; K. DAVIES and HOYLE, ibid., 1951, 233; L. DAVIES, ibid., 1939, 349; M. STOCK and DAVIES, *Trans. Farad. Soc.*, 1948, **44**, 856; N. HINMAN, *J. Org. Chem.*, 1958, **23**, 1587.

9

Stability Constants of Metal Complexes

During the last twenty years, much interest has been shown in obtaining dissociation constants for cations other than the hydrogen ion. The mass action equations are formally similar, but the results are customarily expressed as stability constants, whereas ionization constants are expressed as instability constants. It is convenient to write stability constants (which are the reciprocals of instability constants) as log K (and hence not as pK).

The nature of chelation

Any substance which can bind a proton can bind a metallic cation instead. At high proton concentrations, the proton will be greatly preferred, at low proton concentrations the metallic cation may be preferred if it is present in great excess, or, better, if a new ring can be formed by two groups in the molecule which simultaneously bind the metal. This simultaneous binding is termed chelation, and it confers stability on the complex. If the pH is allowed to rise too high, the free metal cations may be precipitated as hydroxide or as self-complexes (see p. 166).

The substance which binds the metal is called a ligand. There are three principal types of ligands which take part in chelation. The first type (e.g. ethylene diamine) has two electron-releasing groups, and the charge on the metal cation is unchanged by chelation. The second type (e.g. glycine) has one electron-releasing and one anionic group, and the charge on the metal is diminished by one unit after chelation with one molecule of ligand, and by two units after chelation with two molecules of ligand. The third type has two anionic groups (e.g. oxalic acid), and the charge on the metal is decreased by two units after chelation with one molecule of the ligand. The three main types of chelation are illustrated in Fig. 9.1. The arrows in the ring imply that an unshared electron pair is released, e.g. from oxygen, nitrogen or sulphur, to the metal.

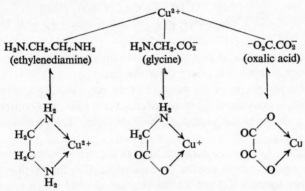

Fig. 9.1. The three main types of 1 : 1-complex

In general, chelation through oxygen or nitrogen atoms takes place only when 5- or 6-membered rings can be formed, and of these the 5-membered rings are more stable. Chelation through sulphur leads to stable 5- and 4-membered rings.

In the presence of excess ligand, 2:1-complexes can be formed. In general, bivalent copper is quadricovalent, i.e. it is saturated when it has combined with two ligand molecules (whether the same or different) thus using all of its four available bonds. The alkaline earths and manganese behave similarly. But bivalent iron, cobalt and zinc are sexacovalent towards ligands of the ethylenediamine type, and trivalent ions are sexacovalent towards the glycine type as well.

Stability constants are determined in order to assess the affinity between various ligands and various metals, a property which varies between wide limits. For the 1 : 1-complex of glycine and cupric ion, K_1 (the first stability constant) is given by equation (9.1.)

$$K_1 = \frac{[\overbrace{H_2N.CH_2.CO_2.Cu^+}]}{[Cu^{2+}][H_2N.CH_2.CO_2^-]} \quad (9.1)$$

and for the 2 : 1-complex,

$$K_2 = \frac{[\overbrace{H_2N.CH_2.CO_2.Cu}.\overbrace{O_2C.CH_2.NH_2}]}{[\underbrace{H_2N.CH_2.CO_2.Cu^+}][H_2N.CH_2.CO_2^-]} \quad (9.2)$$

In each case the formed complex is in the top line, and the substances which form it are in the lower line.

For many purposes the product of the constants, i.e. the 'overall stability constant' (β) is required. If there are two constants, their product is designated β_2, and so forth. Thus for glycine, $\beta_2 = K_1 K_2$.

Writing [L$^-$] for the concentration of the ligand in its chelating form, equation (9.1) can be generalized to (9.3) for glycine, and all other ligands of Type 2. The changes in (9.3) which must be made for the other two types of ligand are obvious.

$$K_1 = \frac{[M^{(n-1)+}L]}{[M^{n+}][L^-]} \quad (9.3)$$

So far we have discussed only bidentate ligands, i.e. those in which each molecule forms only two bonds to the metal. However, ter-, quadri-, quin- and sexa-dentate ligands are also known, and data relevant to these will be introduced later (p. 166).

Methods available

Stability constants may be determined by various methods, of which the most convenient and versatile is potentiometric titration. In this method, the substance is titrated with alkali twice, first in the absence, and then in the presence, of the metal. Because the metal cation displaces the hydrogen cation, the second titration curve lies at lower pH values than the first one. The difference between these curves can, by somewhat lengthy calculations, reveal the stability constants involved.

In practice, these potentiometric titrations involve nothing more than has been described in Chapter 2 or, for titration in very dilute solution, in Chapter 3 (p. 48). We shall confine the instruction given in this chapter to the potentiometric method, but shall now mention some other methods. The best of these are exchange reactions in which two different ligands compete for one metal, or two metals for one ligand. If one of the components is isotopic, measurement is facilitated even in very dilute solution.* A spectroscopic method is also available,† an indicator method,‡ a partition method using an immiscible solvent,§ and a polarographic method.‖ For copper, the copper electrode has been successfully used.¶

Apparatus and solutions for the potentiometric method

Solutions of ligand stronger than 0·01M should not be titrated because of interionic interference. For the concentration range 0·001M to 0·01M, the apparatus described in Chapter 2 is usually suitable. Those who wish to save material, may prefer the semi-micro-method (p. 43). For ligand solutions from 0·0009 to 0·0001M, the micro-method is necessary. Although this is adequately described on p. 43, the original literature may be consulted.**

Only water is admissible as a solvent. Those who feel tempted to use mixed solvents such as dioxane-water, may care to read p. 66.

It is usual to begin the titration with a 2 : 1 molecular ratio of ligand to metal, if a 2 : 1 complex is eventually to be formed in the titration, and a 3 : 1 molecular ratio if a 3 : 1 complex is eventually expected, and so on. However when the formation of insoluble complexes, even at 0·0001M, makes these ratios unworkable,

* SCHUBERT and LINDENBAUM, *J. Amer. Chem. Soc.*, 1952, **74**, 3529; BANKS and BYSTROFF, ibid., 1959, **81**, 6153.
† JANSSEN, *Rec. Trav. Chim.*, 1956, **75**, 1397.
‡ KLOTZ and LOH MING, *J. Amer. Chem. Soc.*, 1953, **75**, 4159.
§ CALVIN, *Experientia*, 1950, **6**, 135; DUNCAN and THOMAS, *J. Chem. Soc.*, 1960, 2814; IRVING and PIERCE, ibid., 1959, 2565; BANKS and BYSTROFF, loc. cit.
‖ LI, WHITE and DOODY, *J. Amer. Chem., Soc.* 1954, **76**, 6219.
¶ DOBBIE and KERMACK, *Biochem. J.*, 1955, **59**, 246.
** ALBERT and SERJEANT, *Biochem. J.*, 1960, **76**, 621.

success can sometimes be obtained* by lowering the concentration of metal ions to 10^{-5}M while maintaining the ligand at 10^{-4}M.

The pK_a is determined in the normal way by adding one equivalent of alkali in ten equal portions, and recording the pH after each addition. The metal is then added in the form of a solution of its perchlorate, to a fresh portion of ligand solution, and one equivalent of alkali is added in twenty equal portions (twice as many as before, because *two* constants have to be determined). The perchlorate solutions are easily prepared from other salts by passing them, in aqueous solution, through a column of ion-exchange resin.†

With many metals, such as ferrous iron, manganese, and sometimes cobalt, it is essential to work under nitrogen. The oxidation-reduction potentials of a metal are changed by chelation, often in a direction favourable to aerial oxidation. The use of boiled-out or (preferably) deionized water increases the precision of the titration in all cases, and is essential when oxidation is likely to occur.

Derivation of equations

The potentiometric method requires the calculation of two functions, [L] and ñ. [L] is the concentration of the *free* chelating species, and ñ (pronounced 'en-bar') is the average number of molecules of ligand bound by one atom of metal. In the titration of a 2 : 1 complex, the values of ñ must obviously lie between 0 and 2.

L is uncharged for type one ligands (e.g. ethylenediamine) which must be titrated in the form of salts‡ in order to have protons for the metal to displace. But charged forms, L^- and L^{2-}, are the chelating species for ligands of types two and three respectively. As type two ligands (e.g. glycine and oxine) are by far the most commonly encountered, we shall state, and then derive, the equation for $[L^-]$. (For glycine, L^- is $H_2N.CH_2.CO_2^-$).

* ALBERT and SERJEANT, *Biochem. J.*, 1960, **76**, 621.
† SERJEANT, *Nature*, 1960, **186**, 963.
‡ ALBERT, *Biochem. J.*, 1952, **50**, 690.

$$\log [L^-] = \log ([L_0] - [KOH] - [H^+] + [OH^-]) - \log P \quad (9.4)$$

where $[L_0]$ is the concentration of ligand originally added, $[KOH]$ is the concentration that the titrant would assume if only water was present in the titration vessel, and P is defined thus:

$$P = \frac{[H^+]}{K_a} + \frac{2[H^+]^2}{K_a K_a'} \quad (9.5)$$

Where K_a and K_a' are the ionization constants of the ligand, K_a referring to the higher pK_a and involving the unprotonated species. If there are three constants, this series is extended to three terms.

Because of the high affinity of some ions (e.g. Fe^{3+}, Hg^{2+}, Cu^{2+}) for all ligands, titration with alkali may not uncover all of the titration curve. Should this happen, a fresh lot of solution containing ligand and metal should be titrated with acid, and $+[HClO_4]$ is substituted for $-[KOH]$ in equation (9.4).

In equations (9.4) and (9.5) the H^+ term usually becomes insignificantly small relative to the other terms above pH 4; similarly the OH^- term is seldom significant below pH 10. When a trial calculation shows that this is so, a greatly simplified version of (9.4) can often be used for all pH values that are more than one unit higher than the pK_a'. However, this approximation (9.6) should not be used without comparing the results from both methods on two readings that are at the extremes of the area to which it is intended to apply approximations.

$$\log [L^-] = (pH - pK_a) + \log ([L_0] - [KOH]) \quad (9.6)$$

The derivation of equation (9.4) proceeds as follows for the common case where the ligand has only two ionizing groups:

The concentration of free and combined hydrogen ions $[H_0^+]$ can be expressed in two ways:

$$[H_0^+] = [H^+] + [L^- H^+] + 2[L^- H^+ H^+] - [OH^-] \quad (9.7)$$

and $\quad [H_0^+] = [L_0] + [HClO_4] - [KOH] \quad (9.8)$

The figure 2 in equation (9.7) is puzzling to beginners. It is used because the species $L^- H^+ H^+$ (e.g. the glycine cation) contains *two* available protons, so that its concentration must be counted twice in order to obtain the concentration of each of these protons.

159

Ionization Constants

The $[H^+]$ and $[OH^-]$ terms in (9.7) usually prove to be alternatives in practice, as do the $[KOH]$ and $[HClO_4]$ terms in equation (9.8).

Combination of (9.7) with (9.8) gives:

$$2[L^-H^+H^+] + [L^-H^+] = [L_0] + [HClO_4] - [KOH] - [H^+] + [OH^-] \qquad (9.9)$$

We shall now state the ordinary mass action equations which describe the ionizations of the ligand,

$$[L^-H^+H^+] = \frac{[H^+]^2[L^-]}{K_a K'_a} \quad \text{and} \quad [L^-H^+] = \frac{[H^+][L^-]}{K_a} \qquad (9.10)$$

When terms from (9.10) are substituted into (9.9), rearrangement gives:

$$[L^-] = \frac{[L_0] + [HClO_4] - [KOH] - [H^+] + [OH^-]}{P} \qquad (9.11)$$

Where P is the term defined in equation (9.5).

Thus (9.11) is equation (9.4) in its complete form, i.e. it includes both the alternatives $[HClO_4]$ and $[KOH]$, as discussed on p. 31.

We shall now give the formula for calculation of ñ.

$$\bar{n} = \frac{[L_0] - Q[L^-]}{[M_0]} \qquad (9.12)$$

Where $[M_0]$ is the total concentration of metal, free or combined, and Q has the value given by equation (9.13):

$$Q = \frac{[H^+]}{K_a} + \frac{[H^+]^2}{K_a K'_a} + 1 \qquad (9.13)$$

Where K_a and K'_a are defined underneath equation (9.5).

When the pH is more than 1·4 units above pK'_a, the simplified equation (9.14) can often be used. However, a trial calculation, by both the long and the approximate method, should first be made on two readings that lie at the extremes of the area within which the use of the approximation is proposed.

$$Q = \frac{[H^+]}{K_a} + 1 \qquad (9.14)$$

There is also a greatly simplified equation for calculating ñ when

160

the pH is at least 1·4 units above pK_a' and 1·4 units below pK_a, and the ligand : metal ratio is 2 : 1. This is equation (9.15), which should be used only after the usual trial calculations (see above).

$$\bar{n} = \frac{2[KOH]}{[L_o]} \qquad (9.15)$$

The derivation of equation (9.12) is as follows.

In the simple, but common, case where the ligand has only two ionizing groups, the total concentration of ligand $[L_o]$ is the sum of five concentrations:

$$[L_o] = [L^-] + [L^-H^+] + [L^-H^+H^+] + [LM] + 2[L_2M] \qquad (9.16)$$

Where LM is the 1 : 1 complex and L_2M the 2 : 1 complex, and all the other terms are as defined above, including the use of '2'.

Because, by definition, ñ is the average number of molecules of ligand bound by one atom of the metal,

$$\bar{n} = \frac{[LM] + 2[L_2M]}{[M_o]} \qquad (9.17)$$

Combining (9.16) with (9.17) gives:

$$[L_o] = [L^-] + [L^-H^+] + [L^-H^+H^+] + \bar{n}[M_o] \qquad (9.18)$$

Substitution from the mass action equations (9.10), which describe the ionization of the ligand, into (9.18) gives:

$$[L_o] = [L^-] + \frac{[H^+]^2[L^-]}{K_a K_a'} + \frac{[H^+][L^-]}{K_a} + \bar{n}[M_o] \qquad (9.19)$$

Rearrangement of 9·19 gives:

$$\bar{n} = \frac{[L_o] - Q[L^-]}{M^0}$$

which is equation (9.12).

The required stability constants (K_1 and K_2), for the 1 : 1 and 2 : 1 complexes respectively, are found by the use of J. Bjerrum's summation equation which relates ñ and $[L^-]$ to the stability constants as follows:

$$\begin{matrix} n = N \\ n = O \end{matrix} \sum (\bar{n} - n)\beta_n[L^-]^n = O \qquad (9.20)$$

where n represents various small numbers, N is the largest value of n, $\bar{n}$ has the usual meaning, and β_n is the product of all the constants from K_1 to K_n.

The assumption that a 2 : 1 complex is not formed until the 1 : 1 complex is completely formed, during the titration, led to the following simplified equations, all derived* from (9.20):

$$K_1 = \frac{\bar{n}}{(1 - \bar{n})[L^-]} \qquad (9.21, a)$$

$$K_2 = \frac{\bar{n} - 1}{(2 - \bar{n})[L^-]} \qquad (9.21, b)$$

These equations have been widely used, but were found to give very few concordant results within a set. The reason for this is that unless K_1 is 270 times greater than K_2 (i.e. unless log $K_1 > 2 \cdot 5 + \log K_2$), then 1 : 1 and 2 : 1 complexes are being formed simultaneously throughout a large portion of the titration. Long experience has shown that it is unusual for K_1 and K_2 to differ by so large a figure, so that a situation is usually present analogous to that already discussed for overlapping ionization constants in, say, dicarboxylic acids (see p. 52). Even the trend in the results of log K_1 and log K_2 is similar to the uncorrected pK_a values shown in the worked example of succinic acid (p. 54). Thus, it is better to use equation (9.20).

The correct values of K_1 and β_2 can be found by the summation of equation (9.20) over n = 0, 1, and 2 for a bidentate complex of a bivalent metal.† This process yields the equation:

$$\frac{\bar{n}}{(\bar{n} - 1)[L^-]} = \frac{(2 - \bar{n})[L^-]}{(\bar{n} - 1)}\beta_2 - K_1 \qquad (9.22)$$

Log K_2 is then obtained by subtracting log K_1 from log β.

Equation (9.22) is an equation to a straight line of which the slope is β_2 (i.e. $K_1 K_2$) and the intercept is $-K_1$. Plotting this graph is difficult when, as often happens, $[L^-]$ varies over several powers of ten. Therefore it is better to evaluate the constants algebraically

* FLOOD and LORAS, *Tidsskr. Kjemi, Berg. og Metal.*, 1945, **5**, 83.
† IRVING and ROSSOTTI, *J. Chem. Soc.*, 1953, 3397.

by *the method of least squares*. This method uses all of the experimental data except that between ñ = 0·95 and ñ = 1·05 (which, for this purpose, is too sensitive to slight experimental errors and should be rejected).

The method of least squares calls for the following steps. First of all, values of ñ/(ñ − 1)[L⁻] are calculated for each pH reading in the titration. These values are called Y, and are added to give Σ Y. (Actually the values of Y are crude values of −K₁ [see equation (9.21), *a*)] and were acceptable as such to editors until a few years ago. Thus, in Table 9.1, where ñ = 0·513, log K₁ is easily calculated to be 8·46, which is fairly close to the correct result. However, inspection of column 8 shows how widely this crude value can vary).

Next, all values of (2 − ñ)[L⁻]/(ñ − 1) are calculated for each reading in the titration. These values are called X, and are added to give Σ X. (Actually the values of X are crude values of 1/K₂. Thus, in Table 9.1, where ñ = 1·493, log K₂ = 7·00. However, many another value of log K₂ could be culled from column 9.)

Next, values of X² and XY are tabulated for each titration reading, and added to give Σ X² and Σ XY respectively. These sums are used to solve the standard simultaneous equations for least squares which are:

$$\left. \begin{array}{l} \Sigma\, Y = n\mathrm{a} + \mathrm{b}\, \Sigma\, X \\ \Sigma\, XY = \mathrm{a}\, \Sigma\, X + \mathrm{b}\, \Sigma\, X^2 \end{array} \right\} \quad (9.23)$$

where *n* equals the number of observations. In the present case, the coefficient a is −K₁, and b is β_2. Thus the solution of equation (9.23) gives mean values for log K₁ and log β_2, and subtraction of these give a mean value for log K₂. But no information is available about spread or trends until the mean value of K₁ is fitted into equation (9.22), and an individual value of β_2 obtained for each value of X and Y. Then the mean value of β_2 should be substituted into equation (9.22) to give a series of individual values of K₁. These individual values are given, as logarithms, in columns 12 and 13 of Table 9.1. No trends are seen in this titration, but in other cases a tendency to form a 3 : 1 complex is signalled by a

163

marked trend. Most workers, when calculating spread, would not use values of K_1 obtained when ñ is more than 1·0, because little of the 1 : 1 complex exists in this region.

Worked example

Table 9.1 sets out a representative determination of stability constants, actually those of the 1 : 1 and 2 : 1 glycine–copper complexes. Details of preparing the solutions, and conducting the titration, were given on p. 157. Values of $[L_0]$ the total ligand concentration, and $[M_0]$ the total metal concentration, have been corrected for dilution effects: this is not essential but increases the precision of the result. Values of [KOH], the concentration of alkali that would be present if the titration vessel held only water, have been similarly refined. $[L^-]$ was calculated from equation (9.4) and ñ from (9.12). The rest of the columns in Table 9·1 are explained immediately above. If needed, lower values of ñ (and hence extra values of K_1 and β_2) could be obtained by a supplementary titration with acid (see p. 159).

Tolerances

Now that the method of least squares is in common use, tolerances as low as $\pm 0·09$ can reasonably be demanded in the determination of stability constants, using at least 14 values for log β, and 7 values for log K_1, in the respective sets. In fact so large a tolerance as $\pm 0·09$ is needed only for log K_2, which bears the added tolerances of log K_1 and log β.

The use of a vibrating condenser electrometer (p. 47) to obtain the third place of decimals in each pH reading, can increase the precision of the results.*

We do not recommend that the potentiometric measurements of stability constants be done at constant ionic strength because the presence of an added salt usually decreases the solubility of the complex to a point where a complete titration cannot be performed. Nevertheless we have been able to repeat the titration of glycine and copper perchlorate at a constant ionic strength

---

* ALBERT and SERJEANT, *Biochem. J.*, 1960, **76**, 621.

TABLE 9.1

Determination of the stability constants of a metal complex

Substance: Glycine, $C_2H_5NO_2$, = 75·07; pK_a 2·22 and 9·86. *Temperature:* 20°.
Metal: Cupric perchlorate.
Concentrations: Glycine 0·01M + cupric perchlorate 0·005M. Glycine (0·0375 g.) (dried at 110° for 1 hr.) was dissolved in 46·0 ml. ion-free water, and 4·00 ml. of 0·06280M-cupric perchlorate $Cu(ClO_4)_2$ was added. The solution was titrated under nitrogen.

1	2	3	4	5	6	7	8	9	10	11	12	13
KOH (0·100N) ml.	pH	$[L_0]$	$[M_0]$	$[KOH]$	$\log [L^-]$	$\bar{n}$	$\dfrac{\bar{n}}{(\bar{n}-1)[L^-]}$ (=Y)	$\dfrac{(2-\bar{n})[L^-]}{\bar{n}-1}$ (=X)	X^2	XY	$\log K_1$	$\log\beta$
0·0	3·21	0·01000	0·005024	—	5̄·2413	0·281	$-2·242\times10^8$	$-0·417\times10^{-8}$	$0·174\times10^{-16}$	0·9349	—	—
0·25	3·30	0·009950	0·004999	0·000498	5̄·3251	0·307	$-2·096$	$-0·516$	0·266	1·0815	—	—
0·50	3·38	0·009901	0·004974	0·000990	5̄·3929	0·386	$-2·544$	$-0·650$	0·423	1·6536	8·37	15·49
0·85	3·51	0·009833	0·004940	0·001672	5̄·5027	0·474	$-2·832$	$-0·923$	0·852	2·6139	8·41	15·52
1·00	3·58	0·009804	0·004925	0·001961	5̄·5635	0·513	$-2·878$	$-1·118$	1·250	3·2176	8·41	15·50
1·25	3·70	0·009756	0·004901	0·002439	5̄·6646	0·583	$-3·027$	$-1·570$	2·465	4·7524	8·41	15·51
1·50	3·83	0·009709	0·004878	0·002913	5̄·7719	0·659	$-3·268$	$-2·326$	5·410	7·6014	8·41	15·51
1·75	3·96	0·009662	0·004854	0·003382	5̄·8748	0·742	$-3·837$	$-3·655$	13·359	14·0242	8·41	15·55ᵇ
2·00	4·12	0·009615	0·004831	0·003846	8̄·0046	0·826	$-4·700$	$-6·814$	46·431	32·0258	8·43	15·50
2·25	4·28	0·009569	0·004808	0·004306	8̄·1294	0·916	$-8·095$	$-17·381$	302·099	140·6992	—	15·51
2·50ᵃ	4·47	0·009524	0·004785	0·004762	8̄·2814	1·004	—	—	—	—	—	—
2·75	4·66	0·009479	0·004762	0·005213	8̄·4278	1·099	—	—	—	—	—	—
3·00	4·85	0·009434	0·004740	0·005660	8·5652	1·197	$+1·653$	$+14·980$	224·400	24·7619	8·45ᵇ	15·45
3·25	5·05	0·009390	0·004717	0·006103	8·7068	1·294	$+0·864$	$+12·225$	149·451	10·5624	8·44ᵇ	15·44
3·50	5·27	0·009346	0·004695	0·006542	8·8578	1·393	$+0·492$	$+11·131$	123·899	5·4765	8·45ᵇ	15·43
3·75	5·48	0·009302	0·004673	0·006977	8·9864	1·493	$+0·312$	$+9·967$	99·341	3·1097	8·43ᵇ	15·45
4·00	5·72	0·009259	0·004652	0·007407	7̄·1407	1·592	$+0·200$	$+9·249$	85·544	1·8498	8·41ᵇ	15·47
4·25	6·01	0·009217	0·004630	0·007834	7̄·2909	1·692	$+0·125$	$+8·697$	75·638	1·0871	8·39ᵇ	15·48
4·50	6·28	0·009174	0·004609	0·008257	7̄·3824	1·791	$+0·094$	$+6·373$	40·615	0·5991	—	—
5·00	8·96											
				ᶜ Totals			$-3·1779\times10^9$ $=\Sigma Y$	$+3·7252\times10^{-7}$ $=\Sigma X$	$1·17162\times10^{-13}$ $=\Sigma X^2$	256·051 $=\Sigma XY$		

ᵃ One half equivalent of alkali. ᵇ Discarded.
ᶜ These values, when used to solve equation (9.23), gave $a = -2·524\times10^8$ and $b = 2·987\times10^{15}$, whence $\log K_1 = 8·40$ and $\log\beta_2 = 15·47$.

Result: $\log K_1 = 8·40 \pm 0·03$, $\log K_2 = 7·07 \pm 0·08$, and $\log\beta_2 = 15·47 \pm 0·05$ (all at 20° and 0·01M ligand).

M

$I = 0\cdot01$, and have obtained results rather similar to those in Table 9.1, namely log K_1 $8\cdot34 \pm 0\cdot03$, and log β_2 $15\cdot38 \pm 0\cdot06$ (at 20°).

Abridged method

A very simple method exists for an approximate calculation of log β, but it can be used only when there is no likelihood of log K_1 being more than (log $K_2 + 2\cdot5$). In these circumstances,

$$\log \beta_2 = -2 \log [L^-] \quad \text{when } \bar{n} = 1\cdot00 \qquad (9.24)$$

Thus, in Table 9.1, log $[L^-] = \bar{8}\cdot2744$, when $\bar{n} = 1\cdot00$; hence log $\beta_2 = 15\cdot45$.

Common difficulties and how they can be overcome

Some difficulties arise from errors in techniques and others from the special properties of the material being investigated.

Errors in technique differ little from those observed in other forms of potentiometry (see p. 40), e.g. the pH set is not properly standardized, or the starting materials may not be dry, or they may be impure, or some of the solution may be lost as spray. If precipitation begins (often signalled by a drift to lower pH values), a titration must be stopped, because concordant results can no longer be obtained.

One of the commonest difficulties arising from a special property of the unknown substance is to find that log K_1 − log K_2 is less than 0·5. Such substances behave almost as though only the 2 : 1 complex is being formed, even at the start of the titration. In such a case, β_2 is the only constant obtainable, and it can be rapidly calculated from equation (9·25), whose derivation is available.*

$$\log \beta_2 = \log \bar{n} - \log (2 - \bar{n}) - 2 \log [L^-] \qquad (9.25)$$

In such cases, β can also be extracted from the least-square equations (9.23)

Another difficulty is that the unknown substance may liberate two protons from each molecule during the titration, whereas we have considered so far only the liberation of one proton per mole-

* ALBERT, *Biochem. J.*, 1953, **54**, 646.

cule. To test for this phenomenon, the titration should be continued until 1·1 equivalents of alkali have been added, when evidence of an end-point should be seen, i.e. the pH should not be more than 0·4 below what is found for the addition of 1·1 equivalents of alkali in the absence of the metal. If no such end-point is seen, the titration should be continued until one is found at, say, 2·1 equivalents of alkali. When two protons are liberated from each molecule of ligand, the substitution of $2[L_0]$ for $[L_0]$ in equation (9.4) is necessary (this effects the correct adjustment of ñ, in turn).

If there are three ionizing groups, the number of terms in P and Q (equations (9.5) and (9.13)) must be extended, K_a always referring to the numerically highest pK_a value, K_a' to the next highest and K_a'' to the lowest. (Sometimes the K_a'' term is vanishingly small.) As an example, the titration of 1,3-diaminobutyric acid is fully described in the literature.[*]

When the pK_a of a group *suspected* of taking part in the chelation is intermediate between the pK_a values of two groups *known* to take part, nothing in the titration figures can reveal whether the suspected group is playing any part. The decision can usually be made from the known stability of the size of ring created by participation of the suspected group, and by comparison of the magnitude of β with the β of a similar ligand in which the suspected group is blocked or absent. The amino-acids histidine, glutamine and aspartic acids have been discussed along these lines.[†] For the calculation of the stability constants of quadri- and sexa-dentate complexes, useful methods are available.[‡]

[*] ALBERT, *Biochem. J.*, 1952, **50**, 690.
[†] ALBERT, *Biochem. J.*, 1952, **50**, 690.
[‡] SCHWARZENBACH and ACKERMANN, *Helv. Chim. Acta*, 1947, **30**, 1798; ACKERMANN and SCHWARZENBACH, ibid., 1949, **32**, 1543; SCHWARZENBACH and FREITAG, ibid., 1951, **34**, 1503; MARTELL and CALVIN, *Chemistry of the Metal Chelate Compounds*, New York: Prentice-Hall, 1952, pp. 88–94.

Calculations of Hydrogen Ion (and Hydroxyl Ion) Concentration and Activity

In potentiometric work, it is often required to calculate the hydrogen ion *activity* $\{H^+\}$ from the pH. This is done as follows:

$$\{H^+\} = \text{antilog}\,(0 - pH)$$

Example: calculate the $\{H^+\}$ equivalent to pH 3·25

$$\{H^+\} = \text{antilog}\,(0 - 3·25) = \text{antilog}\,\bar{4}·75 = 0·0005623$$

In other cases (e.g. Table 2.4), the hydroxyl ion *activity* $\{OH^-\}$ must be calculated from the pH.

From the equation $pOH^- = pK_w - pH$, we obtain:

$$\{OH^-\} = \text{antilog}\,(pH - pK_w)$$

(Values of pK_w at various temperatures are in Appendix II.)

Example: calculate $\{OH^-\}$ equivalent to pH 10·71 at 20°

$$\{OH^-\} = \text{antilog}\,(10·71 - 14·17) = \text{antilog}\,\bar{4}·54 = 0·00035$$

The figures in Table A1 are intended as sighting values and for checking the position of decimal point.

In spectrometric work, solutions of high hydrogen ion *concentration* are often required. These are obtained by diluting hydrochloric acid to the required concentration, because complete ionization can be assumed. In Table A2, examples of $p[H^+]$ obtained in this way are compared with the corresponding hydrogen ion activity $p\{H^+\}$ (as measured potentiometrically and usually referred to simply as pH). These results were obtained at 20°. The temperature correction is only $+0·0003/°C$.

Solutions of low hydrogen ion *concentration* are also often

TABLE A1

pH	{H+}	pH	{OH-}$^{20°}$	{OH-}$^{25°}$
4·0	0·0001000	10·0	0·000068	0·00010
3·9	0·0001259	10·1	0·000085	0·00013
3·8	0·0001585	10·2	0·00011	0·00016
3·7	0·0001995	10·3	0·000135	0·00020
3·6	0·0002512	10·4	0·00017	0·00025
3·5	0·0003162	10·5	0·00021	0·00032
3·4	0·0003981	10·6	0·00027	0·00040
3·3	0·0005012	10·7	0·00034	0·00050
3·2	0·0006310	10·8	0·00043	0·00063
3·1	0·0007943	10·9	0·00054	0·00079
3·0	0·001000	11·0	0·00068	0·0010
2·3	0·005012	11·7	0·0034	0·0050
2·0	0·01000	12·0	0·0068	0·010
1·3	0·05012	12·7	0·034	0·050
1·0	0·1000	13·0	0·068	0·10

TABLE A2

HCl N	[H+] M	p[H+]	p{H+} = pH
0·001	0·001	3·00	3·02
0·01	0·01	2·00	2·05
0·02	0·02	1·70	1·77
0·05	0·05	1·30	1·41

required in spectrometric work, and are usually obtained with dilutions of sodium hydroxide. In Table A3, examples of p[H+] obtained in this way are compared with the corresponding hydrogen ion activity p{H+} as calculated from $f_{\pm}$ (the mean ionic activity coefficients). These data are presented for 25°, at which most of the figures have been obtained.* The temperature correction is large, namely −0·0355 unit/°C. Thus, the pH of 0·01N-NaOH is 12·84 at 0°, 12·13 at 20° and 11·50 at 38°.

* HARNED and HECKER, *J. Amer. Chem. Soc.*, 1933, **55**, 4838.

Ionization Constants

TABLE A3

1	2	3	4	5	6
NaOH M (25°)	[OH⁻] M	p[OH⁻]	p[H⁺]	$\log f_{\pm}^{\text{NaOH}}$	p{H⁺} = pH (sum of columns 4 and 5)
0·01	0·01	2·00	12·00	$\bar{1}$·95	11·95
0·02	0·02	1·70	12·30	$\bar{1}$·93	12·23
0·05	etc.	1·30	12·70	$\bar{1}$·91	12·61
0·10		1·00	13·00	$\bar{1}$·88	12·88
0·20		0·70	13·30	$\bar{1}$·86	13·16
0·50		0·30	13·70	$\bar{1}$·83	13·53
1·00		0·00	14·00	$\bar{1}$·82	13·82
2·00		−0·30	14·30	$\bar{1}$·84	14·14

Ionic Product of Water, Expressed as its Negative Logarithm (pK_w)*

$t°$	pK_w	$\frac{1}{2} pK_w$ (= neutral point at the given temperature)
0	14·944	7·472
10	14·535	7·268
15	14·346	7·173
20	14·167	7·084
25	13·997	6·998
30	13·833	6·917
35	13·680	6·840
40	13·535	6·768
50	13·262	6·631
60	13·017	6·509

* HARNED and OWEN, *The Physical Chemistry of Electrolytic Solutions.* New York: Reinhold, 1950.

The Effect of Temperature on pH of the Standardizing Buffers

Temperature	0·05M-potassium hydrogen phthalate* pH	0·05M-sodium borate (borax) pH
0°	4·011	9·398
10	4·001	9·313
15	4·000	9·270
20	4·001	9·228
25	4·005	9·185
30	4·011	9·143
35	4·020	9·100
40	4·031	9·058
50	4·061	8·973
60	4·101	8·887

The third decimal figure is not significant.

* British Standard No. 1647 (1950).

Calculations of Percentage Ionized, given pK$_a$ and pH

(see p. 9 for formula)

pK$_a$ − pH	if Anion	if Cation
−6·0	99·99990	0·0000999
−5·0	99·99900	0·0009999
−4·0	99·9900	0·0099990
−3·5	99·968	0·0316
−3·4	99·960	0·0398
−3·3	99·950	0·0501
−3·2	99·937	0·0630
−3·1	99·921	0·0794
−3·0	99·90	0·09991
−2·9	99·87	0·1257
−2·8	99·84	0·1582
−2·7	99·80	0·1991
−2·6	99·75	0·2505
−2·5	99·68	0·3152
−2·4	99·60	0·3966
−2·3	99·50	0·4987
−2·2	99·37	0·6270
−2·1	99·21	0·7879
−2·0	99·01	0·990
−1·9	98·76	1·243
−1·8	98·44	1·560
−1·7	98·04	1·956
−1·6	97·55	2·450

(Continued overleaf)

Ionization Constants

pK$_a$ – pH	if Anion	if Cation
−1·5	96·93	3·07
−1·4	96·17	3·83
−1·3	95·23	4·77
−1·2	94·07	5·93
−1·1	92·64	7·36
−1·0	90·91	9·09
−0·9	88·81	11·19
−0·8	86·30	13·70
−0·7	83·37	16·63
−0·6	79·93	20·07
−0·5	75·97	24·03
−0·4	71·53	28·47
−0·3	66·61	33·39
−0·2	61·32	38·68
−0·1	55·73	44·27
0	50·00	50·00
+0·1	44·27	55·73
+0·2	38·68	61·32
+0·3	33·39	66·61
+0·4	28·47	71·53
+0·5	24·03	75·97
+0·6	20·07	79·93
+0·7	16·63	83·37
+0·8	13·70	86·30
+0·9	11·19	88·81
+1·0	9·09	90·91
+1·1	7·36	92·64
+1·2	5·93	94·07
+1·3	4·77	95·23
+1·4	3·83	96·17
+1·5	3·07	96·93

174

Appendices

pKₐ − pH	if Anion	if Cation
+1·6	2·450	97·55
+1·7	1·956	98·04
+1·8	1·560	98·44
+1·9	1·243	98·76
+2·0	0·990	99·01
+2·1	0·7879	99·21
+2·2	0·6270	99·37
+2·3	0·4987	99·50
+2·4	0·3966	99·60
+2·5	0·3152	99·68
+2·6	0·2505	99·75
+2·7	0·1991	99·80
+2·8	0·1582	99·84
+2·9	0·1257	99·87
+3·0	0·09991	99·90
+3·1	0·0794	99·921
+3·2	0·0630	99·937
+3·3	0·0501	99·950
+3·4	0·0398	99·960
+3·5	0·0316	99·968
+4·0	0·0099990	99·9900
+5·0	0·0009999	99·99900
+6·0	0·0000999	99·99990

Index

177

Index

178

Index